W9-AGT-889

love, life

a *mostly* true fable

BERNARDINE ANN TERÁZ STAPLETON

BREAKWATER

BREAKWATER
P.O. Box 2188, St. John's, NL, Canada, A1C 6E6
WWW.BREAKWATERBOOKS.COM

COPYRIGHT © 2021 Bernardine Ann Teráz Stapleton
ISBN 978-1-55081-899-4

A CIP catalogue record for this book is available from Library and Archives Canada

We acknowledge the support of the Canada Council for the Arts. We acknowledge the financial support of the Government of Canada through the Department of Heritage and the Government of Newfoundland and Labrador through the Department of Tourism, Culture, Arts and Recreation for our publishing activities.

PRINTED AND BOUND IN CANADA.

Breakwater Books is committed to choosing papers and materials for our books that help to protect our environment. To this end, this book is printed on recycled paper that is certified by the Forest Stewardship Council®.

I send my undying, most heartfelt thanks to my stalwart rocks. You've coasted with me through all the thicks and thins, the ups and downs, and especially all the sideways. Thanks to the dearest souls: Nicole Smith, Amy House, Marilyn MacKay. Thanks to the wise ones: Beth Follett and Monica Kidd. Thanks to Memorial University for their generous writer-in-residence program. And, I'm enamoured with the book doulas of Breakwater Books: Rebecca Rose, Marianne Ward, Rhonda Molloy, and the incredible team who invest such passion into those of us who toil with the words.

Prologue

Not that long ago, once upon a time when the world was round, I sailed across the sky in a tin can, to Italy. This book began there. I knew then it was a love letter to life, and now it is also my love letter to Italy.

Until we meet again. *Arrivederci!*

A Mollusk in Italy

I'M STANDING ON TOP of a very tall hill in Italy.

This is the tallest hill, if not in all of Italy, then for sure in all of Lucca.

Lucca. Rhymes with hookah.

No one can tell me this isn't the tallest hill of all in all of Lucca because every time I ask *How tall is this hill?* someone barks *Io non parlo inglese!* Accompanied by the withering look. Therefore I say it is the tallest hill in all of Lucca, because as I crawled my way to the top, it felt like it.

There is a thunderstorm at my feet.

A cloud drifts by. It hovers beside me. It speaks rapidly in Italian, in such a manner that I almost but don't quite understand what it says. It sounds like: *Scusi, scusi. Come stai? I myself am very well, thank you for almost asking. I admire you greatly, you little mollusk, as you cling impossibly upon this sun-drenched mountain. Perhaps you noticed me as I hovered above you in a highly desirable configuration of early morning mist? You would be perfect if only you would eat more pasta.*

It says: *You have the eyes of a firefly's last breath.*

A lemon tree, doing Tree Pose, drops a giant lemon on my head.

⌒

I have come such a long way since I found myself in a very arresting situation. You might think that being cuffed and hauled away in front of eight hundred people would be the end. But for me it was the beginning.

One day I decided to adopt a new devil-may-care attitude. I took it on. And now that's how I live: flinging caution to the wind.

Take that, wind. Fling, fling, fling.

I am living dangerously. I count my chickens before they're hatched. I rob Peter and don't pay Paul. I have wine with lunch. Sometimes I have wine *for* lunch.

I walk underneath ladders. I cross the paths of black cats, and when I do, it is they who cross themselves and run away.

I go to the grocery store and take out a bottle of water from the cooler and walk around and drink it before I've paid for it. And sometimes I don't pay for it.

I eat bread.

I am attempting Crow Pose in yoga. I love yoga.

—

This hill overlooks an olive grove, which overlooks the villa complex of Il Borghino, which overlooks a vineyard, which overlooks other lesser hills, which overlook valleys, which overlook ramparts, which overlook the city of Lucca, Tuscany.

Lucca is surrounded by ancient ramparts. They were built to keep out Napoleon Bonaparte.

They failed.

But they live on, while he does not.

Those of us in the know refer to it as the Walled City of Lucca.

It is also the birthplace of the great composer Giacomo Antonio Domenico Michele Secondo Maria Puccini. He of *La Bohème* and *Madama Butterfly*. There is a huge festival here each year in his honour that raises money to pay for a sign wide enough to bear his full name.

If you have never heard Maria Callas sing the aria "Un Bel Dì, Vedremo," now is a good time to do that. Cio-Cio-San, also known as Butterfly, sings: *One good day, we will see.* When the hair lifts off the back of your neck you will have an iota of what it feels like to stand here.

—

There are many places to drink wine and eat, up on the ramparts. This mitigates the subtle (hopeful) feeling that Bonaparte might attack again at any moment.

It was upon those very ramparts that we met our fellow yogis, those luminescent humans. Like us, they enjoy Italian appetizers with unpronounceable names and the sparkle of sunshine upon white wine.

The Nova Yoga Tuscany Retreat group has arrived at Il Borghino. We have pitched up from all corners of the earth. I am here with best-friend-in-all-the-world.

The cells of my body are turning inside out in paroxysms of ecstasy. I read the phrase "paroxysms of ecstasy" once in a Harlequin Romance but never believed such a thing to exist. Now I know it does exist. It is what happens when you inhale wine and pasta through your pores at the same time as doing Downward-Facing Dog. You discover that such a thing is possible, and you're good at it.

Paroxysms.

—

Some of our group have hiked up this mountain-hill. We have followed a steep yet delicate trail of white blossoms decorated with sacred offerings of goat poop.

Wild boars could come charging out of the bushes at any moment.

The magic of this place is such that we could have magically levitated to the top. But no. We had to climb using our limbs. These are hardy souls, filled with such enlightenment and wisdom that they pounded ahead of me, leaving me behind along the trail.

Everyone seems so sure of themselves. Everyone seems to belong. I long to radiate a cloak of serenity and invite the others to nestle beneath it. I am captivated by how casually everyone remarks upon the tricks and turns that brought them here. *To me!* Criss-crossing the planet in tin cans that sail the skies. Calendars perused like tomes of wisdom. Schedules coordinated to the minutest of minutes. People have planned ahead by years! Car pools and caravans.

And me?

How I wept on the way to Lucca. What was the beauty that moved me to tears? Not the lounging fields of farmland, greener than green has any right to be. An illegal, addictive green. Not the wild blooms that cried out to be picked. No.

It was the train.

Was there ever a Newfoundlander not moved by envy, resentment, and grief when faced with a train? When all we have at home are empty railroad beds, where now no trains do lie?

Oh, folly. Oh, Newfoundlandia. Terra Nova. *La Terre Neuve.* A most inconvenient island in the Atlantic, neither here nor there, routinely discovered once every five hundred years, much to the detriment of those already there.

Once we had a train to nowhere, with always the hope of somewhere. Until they took it away.

Perhaps if in Newfoundland and Labrador we had sensibly built some sturdy ramparts around ourselves long ago, we might still have our trains.

The train made our trip to Lucca a lovely romp.

Pieve Santo Stefano. Where olive oil grows on trees and wine grows on vines. I can pluck olive oil and wine any time I wish.

I stand here by myself, but not alone. I am not happy. I am not unhappy. I am in the process of dismantling some ramparts of my own. There is a multitude within me. I feel them.

The Italian cloud says to me: *Here in Italy we are drunk on life. A little wine doesn't hurt either.*

A funny thing happened on my way to here, to this search for myself. Selves. Bernardine. Bird. Bernardini. NeeNee.

My childhood. My poverty. My broken heart.

Everyone has a broken heart. We say our hearts "get" broken. Broken. Smashed. Crushed. Mangled. Squished. Mulched like pork in a grinder. Broken. But then we have to walk around with our broken hearts inside of us, pretending.

Oh hi, how are you, fine I hope, I'm fine too, okay, bye.

If I had a broken arm, I would walk around with my arm dangling at a crooked angle and someone would say: *Oh my God. Your arm! You have a broken arm! Get thee to the hospital!* And I would go to the hospital and there would be an X-ray and then a cast and then painkillers. And that would be good. And after a period of time the cast would come off and all would be well.

—

There is also my telepathy. You will roll around on the floor laughing when you find out how I became telepathic. It is so funny. In a tragically sad way.

But I can't tell you because someone has to die first. I *can* say that it involves aliens, and there was a visitation. It was almost (but not quite exactly) like Saint Bernadette at Lourdes. Who, if you recollect, was in the hills picking berries with her friends one day when she saw an alien. She ran home and told everyone about the alien. Everyone said: *Get over yourself, Bernadette of Lourdes. That was no alien. That was the Virgin Mary Mother of God floating around on a cloud, holding her heart in her hand again. The show-off.*

That is how innocent aliens come to be mistaken for saints.

My Italian cloud, unburdened by saints or aliens, stays with me as I gaze down the mountain. The thunderstorm dampens my feet, muttering about the hobbit-like state of my hairy toes.

I look at my wanton miracle as it sprawls before me. I hold out my arm so the silver bracelet I wear glimmers in the rays of the setting sun.

I am in a spin, the spin I'm in. Free fall. Groundlessness.

Alice is falling down the rabbit hole.

I feel you. I hold you. I carry you. I rob you. I plagiarize you.

For everyone who failed you, I will not. For every time you were alone, now you are not.

My voice. My promise. My plan.

For me. For you.

For us.

Pittman.

———

Those left behind are howling. They are furious. They are eating each other alive.

But I am no longer on the menu.

I have come out as bisexual in the most spectacularly awkward way imaginable. And then flown the coop.

I embrace the fall down this rabbit hole.

In yoga it is important to set an intention. I have three.

In the book *Mrs. 'Arris Goes to Paris*, written by Paul Gallico, the London charwoman of the title has saved all her money to buy the perfect Parisian dress. She has one made especially for her at the House of Dior. When I began to plan my trip to Italy, I felt like Mrs. 'Arris, thinking I would buy only one thing for myself: the perfect Italian dress. I have had an image of this dress in my head since I've been here. It looks like something Sophia Loren would wear. I imagine that when I wear it I will look exactly like Sophia Loren. I will look exactly like Sophia Loren when she made the film *The Pride and the Passion* with Cary Grant. He was the Brad Pitt of his time, but no one looked at him. Because he wasn't her.

I also have to find *The Veiled Virgin*. I'm confident this won't be difficult.

—

I am the third intention.

My story begins one year ago to the day, on the longest night of my life. It was a night when it rained, when I wept, and when the lights went up on stage without me.

A night when I thought about dimming my own precious light.

—

Dusk is settling, as dusk does. Oliver, the Italian beagle doggy, snuffles and turns his dark eyes toward me.

I feel the others stir within me. Cloud and thunderstorm depart for other appointments. In the distance tiny lights dance across the greenery.

One of the first stories Pittman ever told me was a Sufi fable. An elephant falls in love with a firefly and imagines that it shines for no other creature but he; the elephant is confident that when the firefly travels long distances, the elephant remains at the centre of the firefly's light.

I have come a long way to find who I am supposed to be. I hope when I do, I will recognize myself.

A mollusk is a tenacious little soft-bodied invertebrate that builds its own hard shell, like a conch or a clam. In Newfoundland we know them as dark little knobs that cling to wharves, boats, and whales. They are inexplicable. You never see them move, and yet they are everywhere.

Even though this is my first time in Italy, I have seen this view one time before. A lifetime ago. I did not expect to see it ever again. I did not know it was real.

I touch the thread of silver on my wrist.

The past is never really gone. It runs parallel with the present, waiting for the perfect moment to bite. This is how we become arse-bitten.

Take my hand for this journey. I will never let you go.

Come on we goes. I close my eyes.

Heart breaks like rain upon the window

I OPEN MY EYES. I am lying on my yoga mat, trapped inside a Spanx.

I am exhausted, weeping, my heart broken. I am surrounded by the corpses of discarded dresses. Imagine a slaughterhouse where the victims are innocent dresses. This is a dress massacre. The Rapture finally happened. The Four Horsemen of the Apocalypse came riding down through the clouds swinging their big swords and everybody got sucked up to heaven. All that remains in the world is piles of empty dresses.

And me.

I am in the closet surrounded by clothes, with nothing to wear. I have spent hours standing sideways in front of the mirror sucking in my gut while simultaneously trying to stop my Spanx from rolling down over my tummy.

My underwear hates me. Why is it called Spanx? It would be more fun to get spanked. Why am I trying to squeeze into this narrow elastic tube, this body condom? Wearing Spanx doesn't make you look any less fat. You still look fat, plus constipated. Encased like a wild moose sausage.

So here I am, in my rolled-down Spanx, which will not stay unrolled. It is supposed to stretch all the way up to just beneath my bust, but on me it insists on becoming an inner tube around my waist. Which already resembles an inner tube. Now I have two inner tubes.

My Spanx is dysfunctional.

In this moment I am supposed to be sitting down to a gourmet dinner with friends, then capering off to see the world premiere of a new play I've written.

The name of the restaurant is the Fish Exchange. I have planned to eat a very expensive meal of fresh halibut drizzled with a citronelle sauce, served with a side of seasonal vegetables and a salt cod fritter. Fish is one of my favourite things to eat, plus the carb count is low.

I'd rather be on the stage than at the dinner. I was

born with stage fright. About life. I have a chronic anxiety that hums along at about a five on a scale of one to ten.

I didn't speak until I was three years old. On the surface it makes no sense that I would hurtle toward a life on the stage with all the glee of a fly crawling into a pitcher plant.

But I loved being a character onstage, with the words already written down for me. You never have to worry about what to say next, or what to plan, because it is all already written out for you. Like fate. You do have to learn all those words and lines off by heart, of course. There are many lovely words in plays. Who knows what the half of them mean, really. But it does not matter a whit. You just march around and speak as directed, and everyone knows what comes next. Except the audience. It is heaven.

It *was* heaven.

I worked for years on a popular stage show filled with skits and shenanigans. It was an annual event that toured hither and yon and played to scads of fans. Critics said it was lowbrow. In that show there is always one scene that is the cause of much contention within the cast. It is usually written by someone who has the director's favour and is a scene that the rest of us do not care about. It is usually way too long. No one likes it. Not the audience. Not the actors.

I have always had to be in this scene. Unlike others, I was never important enough to refuse. It also usually involved wearing a bizarre costume, like a cow with an udder. The cow is biblical for some reason. With the udder hanging out, because that is comedy.

I stand on the stage trying to be an invisible biblical cow. I'm good at that. I vanish into the background. But inevitably I have to say a line, something like "Moo. Whither thou goest?" and it startles people because they think: *Oh my God, that woman just appeared out of thin air. And she's dressed like a cow.*

It is humbling to be onstage dressed as a biblical cow and to know you are a depressed biblical cow.

There is nothing funny about depression. Except that everything is funny about it. Maybe not funny ha-ha. But there are times when it's funny ha-ha. Such as knowing that it's like the aliens—something that makes for awkward cocktail party conversation.

Hi, how are you, fine I hope.

I'm massively depressed of late. I haven't changed my underwear in days.

Oh, look.

What?

Somewhere else I'd rather be.

In the movies about big stars, like Patsy Cline and Loretta Lynn and Janis Joplin, there is always a scene where they are onstage and then right in the middle of a song they just stop singing and look out at the audience and then start crying and they start telling the truth about how they really are. Then they have a breakthrough and feel better.

Except for Janis. She died.

I fared better as a writer.

———

My new play, *Brazil Square*, is onstage tonight at the iconic LSPU Hall in downtown St. John's. The main character, a boarding house landlady named Mrs. Kent, is serving her boarders salt cod with boiled potatoes and onions smothered in drawn butter. Dessert will be green Jell-O moulded in the shape of a starfish, topped with evaporated milk and a dusting of white sugar.

There are canned peas and carrots inside the Jell-O. It quivers as she brings it to the table. Her *pezzo forte*. Her boarders, her instant and now lifelong admirers, applaud as if they are in the presence of royalty. Which they are.

Brazil Square isn't a square at all but a long, meandering street, which was once a world-famous boarding house district in St. John's. Brazil Square was to St. John's as the Vatican City is to Rome: a heart centre where travellers came to stay before the days of luxury hotels or round-trip visits over paved roads. Mrs. Kent rules over Mrs. Kent's Boarding House and Establishment, an impeccable house known for her charming touches. Mrs. Kent dreams of Italy and eagerly shows off her smattering of Italian words. *Ciao, bella. Come stai? Piacere.* She sets her table with salt and pepper shakers shaped like the *Mona Lisa* and the Leaning Tower of Pisa. Mrs. Kent, as I wrote her, is no bilious landlady, the sort of the hair curlers and dangling cigarette. Mrs. Kent smokes with an elegant cigarette holder and is so glamorous and popular that celebrities regularly appear to have their photos taken with her.

Norma Jean. Cary Grant. Johnny Cash.

The woman in the mirror is pure fiction, and no one knows it. She has almost forgotten it herself. She is completely armoured, only peripherally aware that she is an imposter.

Hers is the face of a movie star. The auburn hair colour is natural, the coral lips less so, but these two attributes combined with her emerald eyes would sell tickets in Hollywood. An air of secret amusement surrounds her like perfume. And something else, something impenetrable, guarded, that saves her from ever being called sexy. It could be described as prim, not prudish, but carefully polite. Her guests often describe her as charming. They disclose their most intimate stories to her without noticing that she never does the same.

Word on the street is that the play is sold out even before opening. It's that good. The actress who plays Mrs. Kent is one of our country's finest, having appeared as part of the National Arts Centre's regular ensemble. She is entrancing. Patrons are desperately calling the box office, threatening and bribing, threatening to bribe, in order to score seats.

But I'm not there. I'm here.

—

When my family moved from North West River, Labrador, to Marystown, Newfoundland (giving me dual citizenship status in my home province), I was introduced to my beloved Uncle Bernard Butler, my mother's brother. I'm named after him. He was a road cowboy. A long-haul taxi driver, back in the day, driving people from the outer reaches of Newfoundland over the dirt roads into the metropolis of St. John's. It took twelve hours sometimes to make the trek. We'd rattle into Brazil Square, the touchstone of our destination, dust-covered pioneers.

Brazil Square was a bustling, welcoming home-away-from-home that was nothing like my home and everything I wanted my real home to be.

Writing the play was a labour of love. A play about the secretive Mrs. Kent who sleeps beneath an oil painting of the tallest hill in Lucca and about the taxi driver, Mr. Butler, who wants to take her there. Mrs. Kent's chiselled beauty and cat-like eyes are the centre of his world, the vision he keeps as he drives the long and lonely roads of our vast province.

Brazil Square was also where I stayed sometimes when I visited Pittman.

———

I realize that even if I can keep this devil Spanx on, if I go to the luxurious dinner, I won't be able to sit down because I'm encased like a wild moose sausage with no wiggle room to bend. I'll have to stand at the dinner table eating my halibut like a thief on the run. If anyone asks, *What the frig are you doing?* I will say, *I like to eat standing up because the food has to travel that much farther to my mouth before it migrates to my hips, which is where I like to store my food for the winter.*

My hips are squirrel cheeks.

I try to rip off the Spanx, but if you've ever successfully stuffed yourself inside one, you know the only way out is death.

I cut it off with manicure scissors.

I'm naked on my yoga mat.

My heart breaks like rain upon the window, or perhaps the rain is breaking there like a heart. I close my eyes. It sounds like applause.

The stage lights are going up at the theatre by now.

I'm filled with clichéd abject despair. I think: *Well, I'll have to go naked to my play because I have nothing to wear.*

I think: *I hate myself. Selves. I'm a blob, blob, blob. I'll never drive through Paris in a sports car with the warm wind in my hair.*

I think: *Where have I been all my life?*

I think: *I don't want to be here anymore.*

I cry myself numb, falling into sleep. I wake with a start at three a.m. to the sound of Pittman saying my name.

Bernardine.

Stalking the Piazza Bernardini

I'M FLUSHED WITH EXCITEMENT, plump and sweating inside my yellow dress. I stole it from a theatre costume bank believing it would give me an air of intrigue. It's retro and sleeveless. Going sleeveless is a big step for me. I've spent years hating my upper arms. The dress is gauzy and long with swirls that look like pretty female faces. I wish I'd worn a slip, because the back of the dress keeps crawling up my butt crack. I keep pulling it down in what I hope are surreptitious moves, but it probably looks exactly like what it is: picking my dress out of my butt. I know in my heart that when I find my perfect Italian dress, I'll be able to walk everywhere without once having to pick at my butt. Also, it will not bunch around my waist like I'm pregnant. Neither will I sweat.

I'm clutching a soggy map of the centre of Lucca. I've studied it inside and out, upside down, right side up. I've drawn the way to the Piazza Bernardini in blue pen. Easy peasy.

Standing on the corner of San Paolino and Burla-macchi is a short, handsome, very old man. He's older than poetry. He's weeping while gazing at a selection of ties on display in a designer store window. He rocks back and forth on his feet. His tears form rivers that run down the crevasses of his face. They cascade to thecobblestones beneath our feet, puddles of tears that the rest of us step over in annoyance. He's dressed to the nines and tens and elevens, Ralph Lauren from head to toe. He's wearing a fedora with a red feather. His long white hair brushes his collar. He's wearing a pocket watch on a silver chain and checks it obsessively in between sobs.

I stare at him for a long while before I take his picture. I also hope this is surreptitious, but it isn't.

I move on, letting the sea of people carry me, mean-dering. Fellow yogis wave from a table on the sidewalk, holding containers of colourful gelato. I wave back but crest along, secure in knowing I simply have to follow the narrow cobblestone path directly to the Piazza Bernardini.

What will it be like, this piazza? Most likely very charming. I envision a riotous garden with a cherub peeing daintily into an alabaster fountain. Old ladies clad in black, smoking, as they catcall the handsome young men in tight T-shirts and tighter black pants. Benches where Italian cats laze in the sun after torturing Italian mice.

My sandals are slippery on the stones, and I marvel at the Italian women as they stride along in their stilettos. I should have worn the comfortable nun shoes I bought especially for this trip. I resolve to wear them hereafter with rolled down stockings (so as not to get blisters), like a stereotypical depiction of a fishwife, typically characterized as a coarse and foulmouthed woman. (I feel sad for all the poor, innocent fishwives through the ages. Usually no one's wife, much less married to a fish.)

In this manner I traverse the length of Paplino. Just when I expect to arrive at where my piazza should be, I see that I have not. I'm somehow back at the corner where the elegant weeping man now sits on a bench, still looking at ties. He's stopped crying. There's a gold ring on his wedding finger, his hands so old the flesh drapes like a glove.

I sit beside him, feeling my dress squish against my sweaty thighs and backside. Standing up will require a ballet of manoeuvres to extract the material. In spite of the heat, he's wearing a camel hair coat over a crisp white shirt and brown corduroy pants. His shoes are dark brown, gleaming leather. His socks match the white of his shirt and his hair.

My own gaze strays to the tie display. I don't see anything that might cause an elderly gentleman to weep. Then the setting sun strikes the glass, turning it into a mirror. He's been staring at his own face, not at ties. Our eyes meet in the glass. He smiles at me while sagely nodding his head. His is the rueful smile of a thousand regrets.

In the reflection I glimpse a head of bushy hair swishing down the lane.

The elderly gentleman pulls out his pocket watch, muttering about the lateness of the hour. I turn to see Pittman's unmistakable form lilting along. Her slightly knocked knees, pudgy elbows, her hair lifting like a wimple in the nonexistent breeze. I leap to my feet and plow through the crowd to reach her. But it swallows her up.

Do you love life?

ISN'T IT FUNNY THAT the scariest time of the day is the middle of the night?

When we say *Isn't it funny*, we mean *Isn't it true.*

It's funny that when we wake up in the middle of the night, everything is true. We have to face our greatest fears.

Every night I wake up at three in the morning, worrying about my credit card debt, how to scrape the cards clean. Worrying about the state of my falling-down house, what will happen after I die. What will people find? What they will think?

Well. Not what would *they* think but more what would *I* think, although I'll be dead and not thinking. But one never knows. I *might* be thinking.

Every night I hope not to wake up for a long time. A lifetime of dying without dying. I want to sleep for sixty years, wake up fresh, new, my hard drive erased and rebooted. My heart drive.

It's funny that when I was a kid, my greatest fear was waking up in the night with the old hag sitting on my chest, reading a book, torturing me. Which she did. Now *I'm* the old hag.

During a pedicure recently, the girl looked up at me to ask, "Do you want me to wax the hair off your toes?"

Talking about my cats at cocktail parties.

Invited to a dinner party where I was paired off with a stuffed sheep in order to preserve the symmetry of the table settings. Even the taxidermy wanted someone younger.

Someone younger in the middle of the night.

I blame it all on Noah. Him and his frigging ark. Everything set up for couples. Guaran-frigging-teed that as they sailed away someone pointed to a lonely figure standing on a rock, glowering beneath her umbrella. "Dad! Dad! We forgot Auntie Tilley!" To which Noah replied, "No, child. We didn't forget Auntie Tilley. She's a single and we've only got place settings for twelve. You knows how your mother gets when she's got to squeeze an extra hand in down at the end."

Everyone from acquaintances to old friends feels free to open conversations in public places with the ever jovial: *So! How's Your Love Life?*

Love Life! Love life! Love life. love life... Echoing through the room.

There's no correct answer for this. If you say it's fine, the room becomes hushed while all eyes turn your way. Sweat trickles down your back while you try to think up a good lie. People don't like it when you reply, *No hope there. Completely unfit for mating because of the hair on my toes.*

They particularly do not like: *I devoted three decades of my life to a misguided love affair with someone who I only just realized isn't ever going to want to be with me. Not ever. Not ever ever in a thousand evers, of which I used up nine hundred and ninety-nine. Thank Goddess I got out while I had one ever left to my name.*

I gave that ever to another someone, a splendid, vibrant, exciting, intoxicating someone who burned bright as a sparkler in my life, as I did in theirs.

Then we fizzled out.

In a world without evers, I'm waiting for someone to ask me: *Do you love life?*

A clothesline in Italy

THERE IS A JACUZZI in our bathroom. Except it isn't a Jacuzzi.

I keep calling it a Jacuzzi, except it's a bidet. Two of us can't fit in that thing at the same time. But it's there and there's no way it'll go unused in some way, shape, or form. Maybe for the laundry.

Our balcony is two inches wide by two feet long. The Italian sensibility is profound when it comes to making the most of a small space. Give an enterprising Italian a tiny broom closet and she'll install a toilet, a bidet, a peeing cherub, and a window box of flowers balanced on a slab of marble so valuable that if you have the temerity to ask how much it costs she will hit you with it.

We're ecstatic about the balcony. We resist the urge to wash out our underwear and hang it out to flap and wave at the endless procession of buses, motor-cyclists, and tourists.

Already we've taken dozens of photographs of clotheslines. I don't know why the sight of Italian laundry flapping in the breeze is so alluring for tourists. We're constantly craning our heads to look at clothes-lines draped from building to building, forming canopies of underwear for the narrow streets.

Everyone is going around speaking Italian. When they're not speaking Italian, they're speaking other languages with Italian accents.

I try not to speak at all so tourists will think I'm Italian and mysterious. Even when Italians say things like, *Please pass the butter*, it sounds like, *Shall we make love in a tender field of lace?*

I feel conversant already.

Hey you! Il cucchiaio! (Hey you! Spoon!) This can also mean: *Come here and spoon with me!* or *Hey there! You look like a beautiful spoon!*

(The spoon isn't important for pasta twirling. Spoons are eschewed. Eschew you, spoon.)

Everyone is sexy as hell. The old people. The young people. The poor people. The middle-aged people. Especially the women, of any age. If you're a middle-aged woman of any age, get thee to Italy. Adolescents will fall before you with fake heart attacks in hopes of mouth to mouth. People our own age especially find us sexy. If you sit at a street café plucking your chin hair, you'll have three marriage proposals before lunch.

The drivers are very polite. They will screech to a halt and cause a fifty-car pileup, just so a little old lady with a broom can cross the street.

I've caused many pileups because I keep darting into the street. When I cross the street, I stop to bow at all the handsome crashing drivers.

When Michelangelo lost his original sketch of the doodads he planned to paint on the ceiling of the Sistine Chapel, someone found it and thought it was the plan for the roads in Italy. Once they were made, it was too embarrassing to admit the mistake, so they left them that way.

The best way to drive in Italy is to hire a driver. You get in the back, sit on the floor, and close your eyes. Sip some wine.

The twisting roads that lead to Il Borghino, for example, are so narrow that if one vehicle meets another one coming, one must back up until such time as there's space for both to manoeuvre past. How it's decided who must back up is a mystery known only to the Italian taxi driver. (And to me, of course, being telepathic myself.)

Each vehicle pauses and the telepathic communication passes silently between the two drivers. One then proceeds to very slowly back away.

Otherwise Italian taxi drivers are not so silent. In fact, you'll never know extreme elation until you've been shrieked at by an Italian taxi driver, one who will only grow more agitated when you ask to have your picture taken with him while he's yelling at you.

This elation is only surpassed by the unbearable happiness of being bossed around by an Italian waiter.

The only Italian restaurant you want to frequent is the sort where they speak no English, where shrieking and crashing noises emanate from the kitchen, where there's no tourist menu. Where they rudely put delicious food in front you that you didn't order and then are miraculously able to translate any language when it comes time to sort out the bill.

We find a restaurant called Ristorante Lo Schiacci-anoci, on Via Amerigo Vespucci. We find ourselves surrounded by rowdy people from the neighbourhood. The proprietor, Giovanni, scoffs when we ask for a menu. He tells us what he thinks we should eat. We eat our weight in pasta. We share two dishes. The first is made of a delicate al dente pasta with fresh clams. The clams are so fresh they should be in a Mel Brooks routine.

The other pasta dish has a subtle cream sauce. Subtle, as if the chef thought of a cream sauce, then waved the thought over the plate. It's layered with mushrooms, which still taste of the earth.

The restaurant is family-owned and populated by locals. We're going to move in with them.

By chance, we've booked into a hotel overlooking the Piazza Vittorio Emanuele. And by "chance," I mean that aside from the yoga retreat villa of Il Borghino in Lucca, the hotel for our first night in Italy was the only place we reserved ahead of time. We have the whimsical notion that we'll flit hither and yon as the spirits move us. This is an ill-conceived notion that we will come to regret later.

It is night and we lie awake and drink red wine to the soothing sounds of the piazza outside our miniature balcony: *motorino*, buses, sneering boys with man-buns riding bikes and scoping out little old ladies to rob.

Soon I'll be seeing the Leaning Tower of Pisa with best-friend-in-all-the-world. *Buona sera*, I whisper to myself, over and over.

Buona sera. Buona sera.

The impossible alone

THE SWEETEST AND STRANGEST love affair to ever happen in Italy began on a rainy evening. It was the unassuming end to an unassuming day that turned out to be very assuming after all.

The thunderstorm was sudden, as they all are in Italy. In a moment, hail was rattling upon ancient stones. The water rose magnificently, as if from an underground faucet. Anyone listening closely would have discerned inside the thunderclaps the strains of "Musetta's Waltz" from *La Bohème*. People still talk about that storm. Artists have gone mad trying to capture it, which everyone knows is impossible. Thunderstorms hardly ever agree to sit for portraits.

Sofia Giacomo Antonio Domenico Michele Secondo Maria lurks in the open doorway of her world-famous trattoria.

It is called Sofia's World-Famous Trattoria because Sofia understands that people don't know what to think unless you tell them.

Sofia's World-Famous Trattoria is hidden down one of ten thousand unmarked dank alleys in Venice. It is a devious restaurant. The entrance, a dark door with no doorknob, lurks across from a canal. A minuscule brass plaque reluctantly displays the name of her establishment.

Inside there is one table, one chair. There is one reservation taken, for one night of the year. This was that night.

And there is one Sofia who makes all the rules.

If a patron wants to eat her *acqua pazza* with a basket made out of bread, Sofia will allow it but will make her work hard for it.

Sofia has the great misfortune to be named after the world-famous composer Puccini, hence the lengthy name. This is one of many sound reasons she has to resent her parents. She loves her first name, because she adores and prays nightly to her patron saint, Santa Sophia Loren. The rest of her name she could have done without. It makes getting a driver's licence very difficult because the entire name will not fit on one side. Or even two.

She would have preferred to be named Sofia the Sweet Saint or perhaps Sofia the Kind. Then maybe she would have turned out to be a nicer person. Or even a nice person. Sofia is formidable because she has accepted the fact she is not a nice person. Not necessarily a bad person, but not at all a nice person. Sometimes when she wakes up in the morning she forgets for one second that she isn't nice and feels quite light until she remembers. She pulls scams on tourists. She has magpie tendencies toward shoplifting precious things. She is beautiful, therefore people automatically assume she is nice. They often refuse to believe her true nature even after she's demanded money from them for deliberately wrong directions to their hotel. She is rigorous with the truth but will lie to inconvenience tourists who irritate her. This knowledge of her own not-niceness gives her a strange intensity.

She is smoulderingly beautiful in a dark, hairy way. Smouldering because there is frequently a lit cigarette between her red lips. Her hair is wiry. Her teeth are crooked. She is as crooked as her teeth.

Sofia is wearing one of only two dresses she owns.

It is a black knit dress that accentuates her curves by politely not clinging to them. The high neck and long sleeves are trimmed with three-thousand-year-old beige Kerer lace. It is the sexiest dress in the world because it carries the scent of baked bread with hot butter melting over golden curves. Sofia's other dress is exactly the same. Once she found the dress she liked best, she didn't see a reason to wear anything else. It is exactly the sort of dress Sophia Loren might have worn when she was twenty-five, or might wear now when she is eighty-five.

Sofia completes her outfit with black knit stockings and sensible black leather shoes of the sort nuns wear. This adds to her allure. Nun shoes are sexy when worn by people with red lips and bushy eyebrows.

Her air of mystery is enhanced by the fact that she wears a dark lace veil to cover part of her face, leaving just enough space so that her cigarette has room to smoulder. She has worn the veil ever since the death of her papa.

Not out of grief. For spite.

Men are drawn to her, constantly bewildered by the blind eye she turns toward them. Women shy away from her because they intuit her repressed tendencies. As a result, she is known locally as the Veiled Virgin, but only in whispers when people have their heads safely hidden deep in blankets, or closets, or coffins.

This makes Sofia the loneliest woman in the world, impossibly alone, as she stands in the very centre of Venice, surrounded by tens of thousands of tourists.

The orphanated girl

PITTMAN, THE ORPHANATED GIRL, was best-friend-in-all-the-world when I was a teenager.

Pittman, with the wildest, thickest dark brown hair, like a birch broom in the fits. It crackled around her no matter what she did with it. The hairdresser would thin and thin and thin it, and still it would rise and rock and roll along her pale neck and round face. (A birch is a wonderfully supple, slender tree from which excellent brooms were once fashioned. A birch broom in the fits is meant to denote an unruly head of hair. In my mind, it means beautifully gnarly, like dreads before they were dreads.)

Pittman, with John Lennon glasses before they were trendy, slightly buck teeth before they were sexy. She was cherubic, slightly round, exotic. Everyone imprinted on her. Especially me.

The first time I saw her, she walked into my grade seven class, sat down, plucked the corpse of a bluebottle fly from the windowsill, and ate it.

All the boys instantly fell in love with her. All the girls did too. Everyone wanted to be her best friend. All our mothers wanted to adopt her, even one mother who already had an adopted daughter. This mother embarrassed us all when she cooed over Pittman, "Oh, I could just ADOPT you!" The already adopted daughter and the rest of us scuffed our feet and tried not to feel jealous, knowing that no one was ever going to coo over us in that manner. Pittman won everyone without trying and could be with anyone she wished.

For some reason she picked me.

Her mother had just died of breast cancer. Her father was struggling to cope with five children. The two younger girls were kept together in St. John's with a relative. The two boys were sent to the infamous Mount Cashel Orphanage. Pittman was taken in by her cousins in my hometown.

Early on she read me Edgar Allan Poe's poem "Alone," about how from childhood's hour everything is shagged up.

> From childhood's hour I have not been
> As others were—I have not seen

As others saw—I could not bring
My passions from a common spring—
From the same source I have not taken.
My sorrow—I could not awaken
My heart to joy at the same tone—
And all I lov'd—I lov'd alone.

In that way we both instantly understood that even though I lived with my family, and she couldn't live with hers, we were both orphans.

She adopted me. We adopted each other.

Our miseries were nothing alike, but we each divined enough to never ask or ever have to tell. She was always reading something that knocked my Nancy Drew books into oblivion, like Sufi fables about elephants and fireflies. Like the poetry of Kahlil Gibran.

I had been praying every night: *Please, God, don't let me wake at three in the morning tortured by ghosts and fears. Please, God, let me wake up looking just like the girl on the cover of* Seventeen *magazine. Please, God, let this lemon juice I've smeared all over my face evaporate my freckles so I'll fit in. So people will like me. So I'll be normal and not a freak who is always looking at girls.*

Then came Pittman. According to her I was a child of the universe. I had a right to be here, along with the fishes and the loaves.

I was skinny as a thread. People called me Bird, but not in a good way. I was coated in so many freckles. *You look like a bird shit on you through a screen door, Bird.*

Pittman worried constantly about turning into a blob. When I was allowed to sleep over she'd show me magazines with covers that crowed: Lose Weight Fast! The Cabbage Diet Works! On those nights she'd pay me a quarter to draw things on her back. I always gave up too soon for her.

While she stared at boys, I stared at her.

After a few years, Pittman left the relatives she had been lodging with and moved in with her father in St. John's. The house had no hot water or electricity. Her siblings moved in also. It was the most chaotic, loving, outrageous place to live, *ever*. That house had hardships to overcome but overflowed with joy and care. I inhaled as much of her as I could when I visited. Sometimes I was allowed to make the long drive into St. John's to do so. In the summer of '75 I made the trip into the city to stay at a boarding house on Brazil Square and visit her as a prelude to leaving for Nova Scotia.

By that time we were both achieving liberation from unhappy circumstances. I was leaving Newfoundland to start a course in radio broadcasting. I had rather brilliantly failed to matriculate from high school, flunked by a righteous teacher for a mark of forty-five in algebra. I was heartbroken. All the popular girls, including Pittman, were going to university, complete with brilliant new wardrobes and boyfriends. My mother, determined that I would make something of myself, had enrolled me in what was then a Manpower-sponsored course. It was a program that worked by paying the student (bewildered me) to complete the course of choice and guaranteeing a job at the end of the rainbow. Choices included Electrical, Welding, and Plumbing. There was one obscure designation with the general term "Broadcasting" taught in Halifax, Nova Scotia. I applied and was accepted. No one thought about the fact that I was excruciatingly shy and could barely stammer more than a few words to anyone I knew, much less function in a strange world called Broadcasting.

By then Pittman and I were both fifteen. Pittman was brilliantly winning a series of scholarships so she could go to university and study archaeology.

She was also hanging out with older men: besotted politicians, academics, business moguls. She was forming opinions about things. Men dropped at her feet and fought to pay her bills and her rent and her tuition. She charged through life at the speed of light.

That summer she discovered *The Veiled Virgin* was living with the nuns at Presentation Convent. In those last weeks before we parted ways, it became our mission to torture the nuns and visit *The Virgin* every chance we got.

Not knowing that our vigils would mark our last meaningful time together, we sat outside the convent while the mists rolled in on little cat feet through the Narrows, and the foghorn purred through the night.

Oh, Lady

I AWAKE TO THE haunting sound of a foghorn.

A foghorn in Italy? What fresh wonder is this? Anything is possible here! Cherubs abound!

I cram my mouth with warm brioche, lick my sticky fingers, lick the plate, lick the little flakes from off the table.

Eating is serious business in Italy. Leave no crumb unturned.

I'm learning a whole slew of Italian words. Such as, in Italy, the first hotel floor is number zero. In Italian, that's *zero*.

(Hotels and landmarks in Italy are difficult to locate. They're sly and elusive. You can't find them by looking directly at them. You must saunter along deliberately *not* looking, and soon you'll catch one out of the corner of your eye. *Prego!* You're welcome!)

I'm infusing all of my language here with as many Italian words as I can learn, as long as they are simple.

What a lovely day! *La prima colazione!* (What a lovely day! Breakfast!)

Here is my invitation: Follow me. *Segue!* I will take you to the Torre Pendente. The Leaning Tower of Pisa.

The best way to walk the streets of Pisa is to dance. Dance as if everyone is watching and no one cares. Because no one does. People will dance along with you in an Italian non-caring way. I dance all the way to my beloved Torre Pendente.

I tried to catch a glimpse of her everywhere I went. I looked for her from the airplane window. From the balcony of our first hotel.

The Leaning Lady hid from me.

I've thought and dreamed and written about her for years. The Leaning Tower of Pisa, in Pisa. Pittman and I dreamed we'd be heroes. We'd see the Leaning Tower of Pisa, visit all the famous landmarks, and along the way discover the Other, the twin to *The Veiled Virgin*.

—

My first impression of the Leaning Tower is that she's endearingly modest. A shy little world-famous land-mark tilting coyly at the end of an unlikely street.

Be still, my heart. My heart is still.

She's tinier than one would think. We come to her in silence. We are a pilgrimage of admirers from around the world. We dance to her together, in saris, kimonos, hijabs, jeans. Strangers joined in reverence. None of us has met before, but we hold hands, and laugh, and clap, and take each other's picture. We will be friends forever without knowing each other's names. Forever. We are giddy. We fritter away endless minutes trying to reproduce the photo where it seems we are holding the beloved Lady in our hands.

The closer we come, the higher she rises. A still but palpable presence, like a saint, or a sex worker, one who stands in wait. She is elegant, like an iconic lady who once wandered the streets of St. John's. She was sometimes known as Marilyn, sometimes as Trixie. Marilyn (or Trixie), depending on the day, appeared from a distance to be an oasis of white-blonde beauty. Her platform heels, her leopard-skin bustier, her painted red lips, her platinum-blonde, teased updo—the blonde birch-broom bombshell. Up close the cracks and muttering were revealed. So it is with the tower. Is she a dejected bag lady or the sly survivor?

So it is here.

Oh, Lady. You had me at *l'aperitivo*.

I take a deep breath. We buy our ticket to enter, get in line, are turned away because we're not permitted to bring our purses inside. We go back to the ticket office to check our bags, go get in line again.

Our guide is named Valeria. Or maybe his name is Delirium because he is so very handsome. He begins our welcome speech in Italian, which all the Italians speak. This he follows by speaking in English with a heavy Italian accent. I'm reeling.

We're all reeling, because the Leaning Tower of Pisa is on a tilt. Walking up and down the two hundred and fifty-one steps, then navigating around and around the exterior, is almost exactly but not quite like trying to walk to the bar while on a Marine Atlantic ferry in a gale of wind. It's like being drunk, drunk on Italy herself, which requires no alcohol.

We stagger to the Campo dei Miracoli in search of sustenance. We find the Via degli Artigiani. The Street of the Craftsmen is filled with restaurants, shops, kiosks, hucksters, and hustlers of all sorts. Everyone doing the best they can to make a living.

The chef who makes our seafood pasta and *ravioli freschi* is a broad woman with a broader smile. She ducks behind a pillar when I try to take her picture.

My pasta is so fresh it had flung itself at my plate.

The white fish and calamari followed suit. The ravioli slaps our faces. We stop eating out of politeness for all the eating we plan to do later.

My heart is crocheting a lace shawl to keep itself intact. With a spoon I stole from a restaurant called The Mafia Pasta Place, using a spool of priceless lace I pocketed from an ancient roll on display in a shop. The spoon twirls the lace until it spins into a dainty web.

I wonder at this feeling of being free. Unfettered. Untethered. I'm not used to this. I feel frissons of fear.

I wear my heavy nun shoes to keep me from floating away.

⌒

The years have been unkind to Brazil Square. The row houses slowly begin to tip to one side, as in a drunken chorus line. It doesn't deter Mrs. Kent. She believes that her boarding house, like the Leaning Tower of Pisa, will find dignity once again. If not height.

She pretends to conduct business as usual, although many of her regular guests have absconded to the new hotels popping up downtown (where not even a cup of tea is free!). Her charming touches of seashell-shaped soaps and crocheted poodles to cover the toilet paper rolls can't lure them back. She hoards photographs of the Leaning Tower of Pisa, to help soften the many years of hard work she has endured. She collects brochures that do not gather dust on her bedside table. She becomes increasingly wary of venturing outside. She deflects questions about her late husband and doesn't like to dwell on things past. She has an oil painting of a vineyard in Lucca on her bedroom wall. She found it at an estate sale, something that bothers her more than she would have anticipated. Another boarding house landlady gone too soon.

I think of my fictional Mrs. Kent while I'm here on the *percorso*. We recline to watch Italian clothes dance on Italian clotheslines. We are served dishes of glistening anchovies, which I try reluctantly and then devour. When I was a child my grandmother hung rows of squid to dry on the clothesline. I hated the smell of them. I hated the taste of all fish. In *Brazil Square* I tried to make up for my ingratitude by making all those dishes culinary staples of Mrs. Kent's. Salt fish with drawn butter and crusty homemade bread for dipping. Savoury salt fish cakes with mustard pickles and pots of tea strong enough to stand a spoon in. Mrs. Kent is very superstitious about her menu and the order of days on which meals are served. Fish and chips is all the rage at the local diners now, and her guests ask for that rather than her boiled fish and potatoes.

I wish I had given her a taste for anchovies. I wish I had given her a happy ending.

A mad hatter in Lucca

THERE'S A LITTLE BLACK bird here whose song resembles Puccini's "Sono andati?" from *La Bohème*.

I made an error while studying the map of Lucca. A straight line isn't a straight line at all. If you examine the lines with a magnifying glass you can discern tiny nuances that are almost (but not quite) swerves, meaning that a new street begins. They aren't named on the map, or clearly marked, but now that I know how to read the map properly, it seems easy enough.

In Lucca we find the church where Puccini sang and where he was baptized and played the organ and where the acoustics are so good, you feel free to sing along loudly with the wrong words in the wrong key in all the wrong pauses, and it still sounds heavenly.

It's a Puccini opera feast. Wine and the babble of the night fill me with optimism.

Sitting at the opera, I'm surrounded by a sea of fancy hats. It's a mad hatter, Puccini tea party, except the tea is champagne. After the last note has finished vibrating through the church, I walk out into the mild evening, striding toward the Piazza Bernardini.

I notice that everyone else is going in the same direction. The hats bob up and down as we walk along. Red hats are worn with green dresses, yellow hats with polka dot dresses, and so on, all the colours the old rules said should never go together are together here for all the world to see. There's been no sign of my perfect dress. I have an image of it in my head, but it doesn't match anything I see on the streets or in the shops.

In the high fashion world that is Italy, anything goes, and everyone looks wonderful. The shops are filled with designer brands so exclusive that if you have to ask who made it, you don't deserve to own it. There are jewelled purses that look like shoes, and shoes that are really hats. There are gloves made out of whispers of cloth, and shoes of buttery soft leather. Yet if you look closely at the throngs of the finely clad, you see that Italians aren't wearing anything flashy.

The dress I seek isn't high fashion. Nor is it cutting-edge. I'll know it when I see it. In the way of all things in Italy, I've probably been looking for it too directly.

I'll have to sneak up on it from the side.

Is it possible that this sea of mad hatters is also going to the Piazza Bernardini? I check my map periodically. Maybe this is a parade I've fallen in with. The babble is comforting. I like being surrounded by a language I don't understand. It relieves the stress of having to think up interesting things to say. Although it might be nice to share with these beautiful souls that I have my very own piazza. To just casually drop it into conversation. *Hello! Lovely to meet you. Would you care to join me in my piazza for a drink?*

We glide past the corner shop where the crying man sits on his bench. He's dressed in the same clothes, as impeccable as before. The crying man isn't crying today. He's cuddling a tiny brown rabbit on his lap. The rabbit is on a red leash.

A woman brushes past me, knocking my shoulder. She breezes on, not bothering with my *Oh, so sorry!* (Even though she bumped into me, not me into her.) She's wearing a dark veil with a cigarette between her lips. I watch her as she strides off, cutting a swath through the hatted revellers.

Who will row the gondolier to the grave of the gondolier?

Sofia stands in her doorway, shimmering in her cloak of misery. She watches people agitate like ants. They are constant hazards to themselves and others by continually coming to a dead stop in busy thoroughfares, getting mowed over, mowing other people over, wreaking havoc. They constantly stop to gape, weep, and take pictures of ancient works of art, churches, statues, and of Sofia herself. Her charisma is such that no photos of her ever turn out. People are left to stare at a blur in the centre of the photo, as if they had tried to snap a picture of a firefly.

In Venice, pedestrian collisions occur at a rate of one every one-point-three seconds. If one were to imagine two thousand tourists crowded into a narrow street with each person crashing to a halt every one-point-three seconds, then crashing into somebody else every one-point-three seconds (mainly because they are taking pictures with a cellphone), one gets some idea of how hazardous life can be in Venice.

Sofia herself has a built-in radar and can part the seas of humanity with a single sultry glower. Fortunately, the only people hurt by tourists are other stupid tourists.

Sofia stands smoking, impervious to the hailstones, the rain, the rivers of water. These elements carefully flow around her, to avoid getting her wet or even damp.

She closes her eyes. She prays out loud.

"Every night. Every night I climb the stairs to my *appartamento* to find that nothing is done. Nothing. No thing. Not one thing. Who will row the gondolier to the grave of the gondolier?"

She waits. There is no reply from Santa Sophia Loren, although Sofia is not too far gone yet to give up hope. Otherwise, why pray?

"No one knows the answer because I myself have not made those arrangements yet. I try to rest, but do you think that my papa will let me sleep? Oh, my dead papa, why do you have to torture me this way?"

She sighs, "Ah, dear God." She breathes, "*Mio Dio*." She is resplendent in her sorrow.

Here is the thing about misery. There is no finish line. There is no event to conclude the suffering.

The unthinkable happens. A raindrop lands upon her foot. The nun shoe, along with the being who wears it, is affronted.

NeeNee appears from out of the mists, like a figurehead on the prow of a ship. (If, that is, that figurehead were unhappy, waterlogged, afraid of water, had matted wet hair and eyeliner dripping down her face in black teardrops.)

Sofia, who is adept at reading people, sees before her an insecure woman who has spent her entire life trying to be good, trying to be the epitome of good. She sees a woman who reeks of sour goodness.

NeeNee, who is not so adept at reading people, has been stumbling around since the storm began in the futile search for sanctuary, lost in the crypt-like alleys.

"Where did you get that dress? That is the dress of my dreams," says this two-legged abomination, this silver-haired, aging, pudgy flower child, her face wet with rain and hailstones, eyes swollen with hidden torrents of weeping. "Do you speak English?"

The two women stand face to face for a brief eternity, one in the deluge, one dry beneath the doorway.

Sofia takes a long pause to blow a stream of smoke into the face of the intruder before she replies, "No." She looks the wretched tourist up and down, as if she may have to murder her.

In this moment, fate careens and a particularly loud peal of thunder shakes the cobblestones beneath them, causing NeeNee to jump inside the trattoria and huddle next to Sofia.

Sofia begins to rant.

"In you walk like you own the place. They all do. Look at this. You come here and you want everybody to speak your language. Why don't you learn to speak our language? Do you speak Italian? No. I did not think so. *Io non parlo inglese. Parli italiano? Così ho pensato!* I do not speak no English. I am just written this way. So! You have to live with it, and I have to live with it," she says in English.

NeeNee blushes, dripping, staring, fascinated. Because she works so hard at being nice, at being polite at all costs, she looks around, believing that Sofia is inviting her inside. Eager to please, she bows a little, as if to royalty, and comes a little farther through the doorway. A fresh spatter of hailstones pelts down, forcing her inside. She hesitates, afraid of slipping. She is not dressed for rain, wearing orange sandals and the sort of long flowered gown favoured by aging flower children. Her toes are hairy and her nails are unvarnished. She blinks myopically at Sofia.

"What are you looking at?" demands Sofia. "Out there, it is a thunderstorm. In here, it is me. If you do not like it in here where it is dry, you can go out there, where it is not dry. This is Venezia. We are sinking and it is raining. If you do not want to get wet, go home."

NeeNee shifts her gaze to Sofia's cigarette. Sofia takes this as an affront.

"Why you look at my *sigaretta*? I mind very much if you want me to put out my *sigaretta*. I mind very much not smoking."

Sofia is wrong. NeeNee is craving a cigarette of her own.

NeeNee glances up from the cigarette and for the first time meets Sofia's gaze directly, her black eyes glowing behind the lacy veil.

Sofia is struck by the unusual shade of sea-blue eyes.

NeeNee blushes, which reddens her cheeks like candy apples. She looks away again.

"In Italia it is required that you smoke. It is very much *richiesto*. In fact, people travel to Italia expressly to be able to smoke. We are the designated smoking area of the world. So, if you want to stay in here with me in Sofia's World-Famous Trattoria, where it is dry, it is my rule that you must smoke!"

NeeNee roots in her bag and pulls out a damp menthol. She tries to light it, fingers shaking. Sofia is further outraged by the sight of the offensive cigarette-pretender. She plucks it from NeeNee's fingers and flicks it out the door. Then she fires up two unfiltered cigarillos in a manner perfected far away and long ago in a film by Humphrey Bogart. She is stone-faced when NeeNee gratefully reaches for the gift.

Their fingers brush. A spark of electricity gives them both a jolt. In the ancient manner of humans divining things about each other without having to be told, they both instantly know that they are women who love women.

Sofia's face might be made of stone, but inside, for the first time ever, her heart skips a beat. As if they were in a romantic film, or in the middle of a book about such things, there is a clap of thunder, then an entire applause of it. Across from the dark door with no doorknob, the water in the canal picks up speed. It rushes by like the rabbit in *Alice in Wonderland*, churning a chorus of: late, late, late.

Donna Summer begins sing "Love to love you, baby." The song comes from across the canal, where a line of people huddle beneath umbrellas and newspapers, waiting to get into a canopied outdoor plaza. A gaggle of white-coated waiters strut around importantly, staying dry beneath the canopy. Other than that, they are doing nothing at all, carrying empty trays.

Sofia and NeeNee watch from the open door of the trattoria. Sofia scoffs. She begins to elaborate in breakneck broken English, "Look over there, where the happening disco music lights up in the night. They play the Bee Gee over there, and the Donna Summers.

Over there, it is The Restaurant of No Food. They never serve no food. They are too busy for food. And yet, look. See how the patrons flock? And the very macho waiter says to them: No. You can't have no food. We are too busy for food. Sit down and drink. And for this they get the very big tip. They only hire the macho men. Only the macho men get to wear the white jacket and serve the no food."

She pauses. "They are too busy for living."

Another pause. "You go over there. You tourista. You belong there. Not here."

Sofia points to the open doorway. NeeNee points as well, to where gondolas bump into each other in the rough current, pulling at their tethers like nervous ponies. NeeNee says, "Oh. Aren't they beautiful! But, I've always wondered. Why are all the gondoliers men?"

Sofia, whose greatest wish is to be the first female gondolier in all the universe, blinks.

She says, "Oh. Hmm. Perhaps you are not such a dim brain."

⏤

NeeNee looks around the trattoria. There is only one table and one chair in the middle of the cozy room.

The floor is burnished red ceramic. There is no counter, no cash register. There is a rustic cooking area in the corner. The room is pleasant, with stone walls that are polished to a high gloss, small trinkets cast hither and yon upon ledges, and one bright red door that leads upstairs to Sofia's apartment. NeeNee takes out a small Moleskine notebook intending to jot down some ideas, but Sofia stops her with a glance.

"They don't serve no sexy foods over there. All the stupid tourists want is the deep-fried Kentucky chickens à la Colonel Sanders. All they want is the stupid poutines, with the cold slaws and the gravies on the sides. I am telling you now. They are stepping on my last nerve. They curdle my dish."

A breadbasket made out of bread sits upon the tiny table. In that moment NeeNee does the best thing possible. She picks it up and takes a tiny nibble out of it.

Sofia says, "You are too skinny."

Ten pounds to happiness

WHEN I WAS JUST a little Bird, a nibble-bibble of a girl, a bite of a girl, a little uncooked incognito kind of girl, the object of all my dreams was to gain ten pounds.

Dear God, good fellow. I need to gain ten pounds so the ogre in our house will stop eating me for dinner.

I would lie in my bed and think of things said. It was exhausting to be me. Every night I died. Every single morning I was resurrected. The breakfast tableau was staged and the family ate together while I tried to be goody-good and eat everything so I could gain ten pounds and my thighs would meet in the middle.

Please God, give me ten pounds.

That ogre is not a booger green ogre with a mildly cantankerous hidden heart of gold. Not bold or easily sold. Not an evil yet stunned ogre the likes of which occur in the Tolkien books. Around the fire they wait for the sunrise. The big sizing up of what makes us tick, the daylight, the day sick. He eats me for dinner every day. Then I am gone. In the morning I am here again, knowing that dinner is coming again.

Growing up I heard: *Don't get a swelled head, stay in your bed, the bed that you made, now you must lie in it.*

My spirit lifting out of my body.

Later, when I learned how to drink, it went right to my head. I'm in over my head.

Give me ten pounds. Which God did. I gained them. I lost them. I gain them. I lose them. I gain them. I lie in my bed, to my bed I am wed. I know the refrain of the pain when it says: you made this bed.

Ten pounds to happiness.

—

Pittman had an instinct for ferreting out eccentric authors. Taylor Caldwell was a favourite. Pittman carried around *The Romance of Atlantis* like it was a bible, and it was, to us. We read the pages over and over, convinced that the alien spaceship I'd once seen was from the lost continent of Atlantis. Pittman thought that Newfoundland might once have been a part of that lost kingdom. Thus, our being "different" meant that we were special. Touched by divine powers.

We read a lot of Taylor Caldwell. *Dear and Glorious Physician*, about St. Luke, further deepened Pittman's desire to work with Mother Teresa. Taylor Caldwell herself was fascinating, with her belief in reincarnation, past lives, her prolific writing career.

Pittman was also reading *On Death and Dying* by Elisabeth Kübler-Ross. She was convinced there was life beyond death, and redemption in reincarnation. We terrorized our schoolmates by holding séances in the school locker room. We'd turn out the fluorescent lights and sit cross-legged in a circle. The darkness was complete in the windowless room. Sometimes we heard knocking, or rustling, or sighs from different parts of the room. We tried to levitate each other. This worked once, briefly, either in reality or in our imaginations, before we ran screaming into the hallway.

And of course, there was always our dear friend Poe.

> Then—*in my childhood—in the dawn*
> *Of a most stormy life—was drawn*
> *From ev'ry depth of good and ill*
> *The mystery which binds me still—*

When I was young-young, I obsessed over *Alice in Wonderland* and *Alice Through the Looking-Glass*.

There is a character in the first called the Queen of Hearts who is a blind fury. She plays a mean game of croquet using hedgehogs for balls, flamingoes as mallets. She shouts at everyone: *Off with her head! Off with her head!*

A lady in my small town went crazy. She was a teacher. Catholic. She left her asshole husband, got a divorce, shacked up with a non-asshole Protestant. She got fired from her job. She lost custody of her kids. Everyone said she was off her head.

They said: *She's off her head. She had to go into the Mental in the city.*

At a moist and tender age I deduced that when you went crazy, you went into the Waterford Hospital for Mental and Nervous Disorders, where they took off your head.

Her name was Alice, the headless teacher. Those were the days when nervous breakdowns became popular. Women gave up in herds, embraced bad nerves, relieved themselves of whips and chains.

A friend of my mother's took to her bed, refused to get up. She didn't have to go into the Mental. She was unsound. Her son and her husband had to fend for themselves. That was the term people used. When Janice refused, had the bad nerves, went off her head, the son and husband had to fend for themselves.

Women dropped like flies. All over the town, men and children were forced to fend. It was a tsunami of dropping crazy off her head fending.

There is the Red Queen in *Through the Looking-Glass*, who is a chess piece. She's crass. She speaks in riddles with constant interruptions and nonsensical questions such as, "How many flowers do you have to pick to make a loaf of bread?" "How many acres do you need to grind the flour?" The Red Queen is all about fending.

Those books are all about the art of going off the head.

There was no going off the head allowed in my family. I had an aunt who so badly wanted to go off her head, the sheer force of repressing the urge caused all her hair to fall out. She took to wearing a horrible, cheap wig, which sat askew on her head. She got herself a demented poodle she named Bijou, walked to the grocery store once a day, every day, to buy packages of Tetley tea and salted soda crackers. Her house was filled with boxes of Tetley tea and salted soda crackers.

She carried her poodle around in her purse. She had a purse poodle before it was fashionable.

The ogre forbade any going off the head in our family. I desperately wanted to go off my head, but not being allowed to, I immediately developed the mumps, then the measles, then the yellow jaundice, then an abscess in my breast, then chicken pox. My body under siege for all of my life while my head remained most determinedly on, not off.

Alice (the one of our town, not of the books) became an object of pity once she returned from the Mental. Having gone off the head, she was no longer able to show her face. Horrible to lose your head but keep your face, even perhaps to lose everything except your smile, such as with the Cheshire cat.

I recognized that rabbit hole. The rabbit hole that occupied our lives was filled with darker creatures than even Lewis Carroll could imagine. We tried to get away from his sharp teeth. We lived where heaven and hell chose to meet. People said: *What a good ogre.* We were chewed to the bone by his appetites, devoured, scoured and tired from holding up the walls of facade, the brocade of lies.

I still worry and worry about that ten pounds.

I take to my bed.

On the television there is a show. All the women die in the show. It is solved every week, these deaths. One day they say: *He cut off her head.*

They say the weight of a woman's head is around ten pounds.

I stand on the edge of this knowledge, awakening, having forsaken myself, my selves.

I slowly reach up and I screw off my head.

Looking, not looking

THE CITY OF FLORENCE has a very special patron saint. Her name is Saint ReFrainius. She's the patron saint of the vendors of Firenze. She's the Patron Saint of Vendors Who Suffer the Plagues of Bewildered Tourists.

The innocent Vendor, upon watching the Bewildered Tourist approach humbly, map in hand, desperate for directions, will immediately burst into prayer.

Oh, dear God, not me, don't choose me, dear God, another one, dear God, why must you cast this burden upon me three thousand and fourteen times a day? Haven't I suffered enough? Please refrain from asking me. Please refrain. Smite me now, God. Followed by a sigh.

Yesterday a vendor wept when she saw me coming. Then she threw herself to the ground and prayed the prayer to Saint ReFrainius. After several hours of this, during which time I didn't go away, she arose and humoured me, as they do.

She drew squiggles on my crumpled map with a pen.

Which is how we came to spend two hours circling the city centre, looking for our boyfriend, *David*, who lives in the Galleria dell'Accademia, which, in theory, was only a ten-minute stroll away from our Hotel City. Ha ha. Along the way we saw the Duomo, the Cappelle Medicee, the Museo Nazionale di San Marco. All by accident.

If we'd deliberately been looking for any of those things, we would not have found them. Things in Florence have a habit of retreating slightly out of view if you look directly at them.

We also encountered a hostile mime who was so cleverly made up that she resembled one of the many precious statues on display. (Or maybe all the statues were hostile mimes who were frozen that way because of boredom and a lack of respect from the multitudes.) She was a pregnant hostile mime. We didn't understand that if a mime sidles up to you and begins to build an imaginary wall around you while taking your phone out of your hand and waving it around as if they will throw it away then you must give them money. We didn't understand, so she was forced to abandon her mime-hood vow of silence and scurry after us screeching about stealing food from out of the mouth of her unborn child.

Inconveniently, there are no signs proclaiming *This Way For The Naked Statue Guy!* When we finally do enter the Galleria dell'Accademia we have to compete and jostle with hundreds of wimpled nuns to get close to *David*. It's clear we are all trying very hard not to look at his penis. Or, we are all looking at his penis while trying to appear to not be looking. Such a tiny, precious penis. Later I discover that size was everything in ancient times. Smaller being the preferred choice.

I abandon *David* to go look in every ancient nook and cranny, but there's no sign of *The Veiled Virgin*. Virgins abound, no doubt. Virgins with arms, without arms, with hearts outside of bodies, without hearts, with cherubic infants, with snakes, apples, clouds, tortured gazes, profound gazes, rising, falling, reclining, drunken, but no *Veiled Virgin*.

—

In Montecatini Alto there's an old hotel that is invisible.

It's a situation very similar to the tale of *The Emperor's New Clothes*. Except in the case of the emperor, his new clothes were invisible. In Montecatini Alto, the old hotel really is there, but everyone pretends not to see it.

Montecatini Terme is a small, precious town between Lucca and Florence. We overnight at the charming Hotel Alforno, made even more charming by our host there, Ricardo.

Ricardo is debonair, handsome, and completely courteous in an old-fashioned manner. He suggests we take the *funicolare*. Best-friend-in-all-the-world says, "Oh! A gondola?"

Ricardo says "No! A *funicolare*!" in a charming yet stern way.

A *funicolare* is a tiny little train that trundles up and down the mountain of Montecatini Alto, which is huge but not as tall as the tallest hill of Lucca.

Once I arrived at the top, I couldn't stop asking: "What's that giant ugly thing on top of the mountain?"

Random resident: "What giant ugly thing?"

Me: "The big brick, ugly, institutional-looking building sitting right on top of this mountain."

Random resident: "Oh, I do not see what you are looking at. Hmm. Look over there. An apparition of the Virgin Mary Mother of God floating on a cloud."

Me: "It isn't an apparition of the Virgin Mary Mother of God floating on a cloud. It's an alien. You can't fool me with that."

Random resident: "Look! An Italian count wants to kiss you!"

Me: "How do I go see that thing?"

Random resident: "There is no thing. There is only the soft breeze gently riffling your hair, which makes you long for Prosecco."

Finally we find someone who tells us that the big, ugly brick building that no one sees perching on top of the mountain is the Hotel Paradise. It (allegedly!) used to be owned and operated by the Mafia. The government closed it down, and now it sits abandoned, a monument to shame and denial. No one will admit to its being there. (Except the one person who does, and I'm not allowed to disclose whom.)

In Montacatini there's no *Veiled Virgin*. In fact, there are no virgins at all. People are born unvirginated and are therefore relieved of that particular affliction.

———

At this point I can't stress enough that it's important to always, always plan ahead. Book ahead. Or else you risk having to sleep in hell.

Which is what happened to us in Venice. More on that later.

———

Montacatini is a fashion capital of the world. We gape as each shop window becomes more and more amazing, outrageous, ridiculous, expensive. The mannequins are ancient aliens straight from Atlantis, hiding in plain view. They wear shoes for earrings, earrings on their toes, gloves of diamonds on their long, birch-broom twig fingers. They wear purses on their heads and hats for bras. They wear dresses of pearls and necklaces of mollusks holding hands.

Desperate for sustenance, we head for a beautiful outdoor patio swarming with busy waiters. They're all wearing white jackets and holding empty trays. We march up to the maître d' who sneers: "We have no food. We are too busy for food." I coin it The Restaurant of No Food as we trundle ourselves into the Americano Café, which has a giant pink pig in the lobby. We sit on the patio with many Americans who are eating cheeseburgers. We get drunk on very dry vodka martinis with three olives in each. We have seven of those. Each.

A sad waiter named Frederico writes his telephone number on my receipt. He tells me he is the loneliest waiter in all the world, as we gaze over at the throngs who happily starve at The Restaurant of No Food.

Cod is queen

PERHAPS IT IS THE fact she can't remember the last time she had a decent rest. Perhaps it is the fact that the macho men at The Restaurant of No Food remind her of the macho men who are the gondoliers. Perhaps it is the fact that the ghost of the macho gondolier who was her papa never shuts up, nattering from where he roosts on a beam in the corner of the ceiling. Sofia has made the split-second decision to cook for this hopeless, too-good woman. She pulls out the one chair and gives NeeNee another withering look. NeeNee does not wither. As she sits, she finds that she is miraculously dry.

It is clear to NeeNee that this meal is not going to follow her usual pattern of reading and writing quietly in a corner while life goes on around her. This is not going to be a solitary experience. This realization begins when Sofia plops a plump, whole codfish on the tiny table in front of her. NeeNee sits, holding the edible breadbasket in her lap, the unfiltered cigarillo burning between her lips. The glistening fish winks at her.

Dinner is going to be fresh.

They smoke for a minute, then Sofia douts her cigarette on the head of a priceless statue and grabs a sharp knife. She begins to expertly gut and debone the cod. The knife slices the steel-coloured fish as if it were a cloud. She tips the bones and the cheeks and the tongue into a simmering pot, fragrant with wine and herbs.

The waves of rain and the disco music wash over NeeNee like a balm. She is reminded of another night of rain, but that night had no adventure in it, only despair. She realizes she doesn't have to respond to Sofia at all, or if she does, she can say anything she likes. She can be completely herself. She doesn't have to try so hard to be seen. She doesn't have to listen so hard or come up with appropriate responses or bend her head in a sympathetic manner.

She takes another little nibble, then another, from the basket made of bread.

She says the first thing that comes to mind. Which is: "Where I come from, cod is queen. Newfoundlandia."

She points to herself and repeats, "Newfoundlandia."

She thinks, *Have I come all the way here to eat a Newfoundlandia codfish in Venice?*

Devil may care

THE QUESTION "DO I look fat in this?" was never originally spoken by a woman. It came from an ad campaign targeting women, to get them to go out and buy a girdle. Which is an archaic fashion torture device women used to lace and strap and cinch themselves into every single day. It was the original form of birth control.

Thank God we've come past that now. Now that we can go Spanx ourselves.

The Veiled Virgin doesn't wear Spanx.

Pittman was never fat. She thought she was. Her favourite pig-out takeaway was Scamper's fee and chee with malt vinegar on the chips. Mine was the cheeseburger platter with the works, including fried onions, dressing, gravy, and canned green peas on the fries.

Pittman worried so much about her weight. She was terrified of being a blob. I ate with impunity. She envied me. I was ugly. I knew I was ugly and way too skinny. It was painful sometimes, to stand to one side, invisible, while she shone. But even that type of pain, the pain of unrequited love, is exquisite.

For a long time I've had a refrain going through my head like the line of a song. It goes: *Do I look fat in this? Do I look fat in this: My body?* It's given me insomnia.

Insomnia is insidious. It only strikes at night. I lie sleepless in my bed, where I lie not sleeping. I lie on my bed that I made (unmade) alone except for my book, my phone, my laptop, my remote control, my glasses, my glass of wine, and my two cats.

And my imaginary dog named Devil. Devil is a good dog. Devil may care.

Devil is a golden brown standard poodle with one slightly crossed eye and a sweet disposition except for when she senses a misuse of the word *irony*.

If only insomnia would strike during the day. Who couldn't use a few more sleepless hours during the day? Because being sleepless then would be a bonus. More things would get done. Or at least the potential would be there to get more things done.

In the middle of the night, with insomnia raging,

I lie on my bed and stare at the ceiling and think: *I'm fat. I'm an alcoholic. I'm alone.* Which translates to: *I'm hungry. I'm hungover. I'm lonely.* A multiple-choice question, where the right answer is D: All of the above.

The little voice inside going: *You, you, you. You're such a failure. You can't even sleep properly.* It goes: *You're stupid and stunned and not very bright and let us not forget ugly and ignominious. I'm saying ignominious to upset you because you don't even know what it means.* And then the voice laughs: *Ha ha ha.*

There's another voice that says: *There's leftover pasta in the fridge. You were saving it for tomorrow, but frig tomorrow. Who says there'll be a tomorrow? No one should ever save anything for tomorrow. If the world ends you'll die here alone, lonely, hungover, and hungry. At least we can do something about the hungry part.*

And then the first voice chimes in: *Plus, you are poor.*

If Oprah Winfrey can't lose the weight, what chance do we mere mortals have? Oprah spent forty million dollars to lose fifteen pounds. She lost fifteen pounds on Weight Watchers, and she got so excited she bought shares in the company and now she owns the joint. In Weight Watchers, you pay them so you can lose weight. You pay Oprah Winfrey.

There's also Jenny Craig. If you pay her money, Jenny Craig will cook your meals and mail them to your house in envelopes and then call you on the phone and tell you when to eat and when not to eat your envelope. Jenny Craig isn't a real person. It's the name of a company called Jenny Craig. It's a ploy to trick you into thinking that you have a friend. A friend to whom you pay money to be your friend.

There's a diet plan called the 21-Day Fix, where you join up and pay a lot of money and then a lady sends you a bunch of faux Tupperware containers. You can buy them from the dollar store, but she sends them to you with a markup and then tells you what to fill each container with. You put them in the fridge, and when you want to eat something you take one out and eat from it.

I filled up all the containers with Cheezies, and then I put them all in the fridge and took them all out and ate the Cheezies.

There's the paleo diet, which says the best way to eat is how our ancestors ate: meat and plants. My ancestors were Irish, so all they had to eat were potatoes. There's definitely no potato diet.

Self-hatred makes you invisible to your own self.

The rushing inevitable

THE COD BEING POACHED in white wine is a venerable cod. A cod so ancient, Jesus walked upon her back. That is how he walked upon the waters. The cod were his obedient stepping stones.

It is for this reason the cod sing as they mate. They sing to each other, and they dance. They return year after year to the same grounds from whence they spawned, to sing and mate. It's a big fish romance. Millions and millions of eggs they lay, billions and billions.

Not many survive. All the cod that are still in the water are little miracles.

This fish, like one of the women at the table, has travelled a long way to be here. This fish, like both women at the table, has known a solitary life.

NeeNee is lost in the elaborate unknowing of what she is doing, the not knowing of what exactly is happening around her. She feels almost entirely like someone who is not herself, or perhaps someone who might be herself. This is a most unusual feeling. She hasn't thought once about being good, not even remembering that she has forgotten to put the other person ahead of herself. She eats the basket made of bread, drinks the wine, and doesn't find it odd that the glass never goes empty. She loses herself in the steady Italian patter mixed with broken English. That, mingled with the cigarette smoke, soothes her. The thunderstorm, peevy at being left outside, directs the water to begin trickling over the doorstep.

She longs to peek in a mirror to see if any of the changes of her soul are reflected in her face. She longs to take out her journal and write down inspiring things. She longs to lift the veil of the chain-smoking Sofia.

She does none of these things. Sofia is saying something in rapid Italian that sounds like: *You are the ambrosia of a firefly's tears.*

The candles around them come to life with a little hiss.

"That smells so good." NeeNee says. "So very

good. I'm starving. I've been starving for years."

Sofia nods to indicate a complete understanding when in fact there is no comprehension at all. Each woman is by now only half-listening to the other, each one only hearing what she wishes to hear.

NeeNee is surprised to realize that she has stopped crying. It is impossible to smoke and cry at the same time, but even so, she tries to squeeze out a tear and none will come. She has been weeping ever since her girlfriend said "You never show any emotion" and left her, thereby unleashing all the hitherto-hidden emotions, useless now with no one to witness them.

NeeNee has not long been out to herself, not long out of the closet, and had naively believed that lesbians did not break each other's hearts. Women would not do to women what men did to women, surely. She had also believed that at her advanced age no one would care which sex she preferred to love. Hence, more weeping caused by a family that cared very much about appearances and what the neighbours would think.

Sofia says, in Italian, "I don't slave over this fish so that the No Eaters at The Restaurant of No Food can disrespect me this way. That noise. This fish is fresh. Not salted."

NeeNee nods energetically, thinking she recognized a word. She says, "I'm lost. I'll never find my way back to the hovel. This rain. Best-friend-in-all-the-world is at the casino. She likes to gamble alone."

Sofia says, still in Italian, "Salt fish, you have to acquire that taste. It takes every skill to prepare. If it's been salted and dried to preserve it, in order to cook it you have to embark upon the journey of the soak to make it come alive again. This can take me days, to check and change the water and check again. But for you, Newfoundlandia, I make it fresh."

NeeNee smiles to hear the word *Newfoundlandia*.

Sofia is slicing baby potatoes into pieces so thin they float in the air around her. Woody leeks twine themselves in NeeNee's hair to form fragrant braids. The air itself is edible.

Neither woman has any idea of the rushing inevitable hurtling toward them, the future coming in hard, ushered in by the Puccini thunderstorm.

Sofia says, now speaking in English, "You soak salt fish too much, it is too fresh, but too little and it is too salty. Now I layer the potato and the leeks just right into the very same pan and we poach it all together. Then we take the jus we make from the bones, the liqueur."

"That smells like drawn butter," offers NeeNee.

Sofia raises her eyebrows.

NeeNee smells the air with appreciation. "Drawn butter is called drawn butter because that's what it's called. So it's no use asking me why."

Sofia has no intention of asking anything at all about drawn butter. Sofia says, "We pour the jus, the liqueur, over that fish and potato and leek, and what results is heaven on a plate. That cod will sing."

She works her magic. "I am going to tell you something now you may find very hard to believe. I am 'a gay.' I am the only 'a gay' in all of Italy. Which make me the loneliest woman in all of the world."

NeeNee sighs at hearing this, recognizing the melancholy. When Sofia looks at her a little too long for a gloriously uncomfortable minute, they both lean further into their mutual understanding.

NeeNee settles into her own skin. Sofia's face of stone softens noticeably. Sofia looks up, speaking loudly as if to someone who might be sitting on the ceiling.

In fact, someone is.

How not to come out in society

LET ME COUNT THE WAYS.

Don't post it on Facebook before you've told everyone in person.

Don't tell anyone in person until you've told everyone in person.

Don't tell some people before you tell other people.

Do tell everyone in your life at exactly the same time, but in private.

Don't tell people in a situation where they don't have time to process it.

Don't tell some people in writing.

Never ever do it in a text.

Don't take out a death notice for your old self.

Don't take out a birth notice for your new self.

Don't throw yourself a debutante's ball, parade into a ballroom to curtsy and bow, officially out.

Don't fall madly in love, then break up.

Don't be an astronaut off the tether, as in movies, floating around forever alone, until you run out of oxygen, circling forever out, out, out of love.

—

"Someday" was the promise Pittman and I made, to *The Veiled Virgin* and to each other.

Someday. One day. When. Not if. We would find the twin in Italy and make a sacred connection between Newfoundlandia and Italia.

We would be dressed to the nines, me in a dark purple, crushed velvet dress with puffy sleeves, like the kind that Stevie Nicks wore, and Pittman in faded Levi's and a brown suede jacket with long fringes dangling from the sleeves. (These jackets were highly coveted but not worth the expense because boys would chase us around plucking the fringes from off the sleeves.) I would not be too skinny and Pittman would not be too fat. We didn't have the details worked out about how we would reunite the two sisters, but we felt sure those things would fall into place once we became famous for our discovery.

We also didn't know exactly how to try to track the provenance of the other sculpture, as Giovanni Strazza had faded into obscurity, along with a lot of other brilliant artists, and there is almost nothing known about him or the legacy of his work.

Unbelievably, *The Veiled Virgin* was shipped and arrived safely in St. John's, all the way from Italy, on December 4, 1856. She must surely have had an escort of codfish to have survived those perilous seas.

She was welcomed and paid for by the bishop at the time, John Thomas Mullock, who wrote in his journal: *Received safely from Rome, a beautiful statue of the blessed Virgin Mary, in marble, by Strazza. The face is veiled and the figure and features are all seen. It is a perfect gem of art.*

But why? Why Giovanni Strazza, a very famous sculptor of the time, would create a priceless work of art and ship her off into obscurity is unknown.

How much did the church pay for her, at a time when most residents of the Colony of Newfoundland were living in desperate poverty?

My theory is that Strazza was a starving artist, so he probably needed the money.

The nuns at the convent where we went to visit *The Virgin* had cultivated the rumour that Strazza had been sly. He had made two. The one that lives in St. John's, and a twin, The Other, who remained behind in Italy.

In our examination of Italian sculptures in *Encyclopedia Britannica*, Pittman and I wondered over how luxe all the female forms were. How lush, solid, flesh spilling over, how incandescent was beauty.

Why, then, did we turn such ruthless judgments on our own precious selves?

—

I'm out, I'm out, wherever I am.

Wherever am I? Officially out of the closet, that closet of clothes, standing outside my own life, nothing to wear and nothing left to fear.

Don't bet your life on your only life. Step out. Step in. I step back into my only life.

I wonder if I ever will screw my head back on right.

Sofia's prayer

"ANOTHER DAY, IT COME and go, and still nothing is done. No thing. Not one thing. When I die, I will be so lucky to be buried on San Michele, the Island of the Dead. I will be packed off to Sant'Ariano, the Island of Bones. Because I will be 'a dead' and then there will be no one to make any funeral arrangements. Not for me the resting place of Ezra Pound or even Igor Stravinsky. I spit on Igor Stravinsky. A funeral to plan and nothing done. That big gondolier will not let me rest."

"Is there someone else here?" NeeNee asks, standing, pointing upward.

Sofia shushes the question, motioning NeeNee to sit back down. "What do you mean, to whom am I speaking? I am praying. I am praying to my patron saint, Santa Sophia Loren!"

NeeNee remains standing, hands clasped at her heart, smiling, wanting to jump. "Sophia Loren? Sophia Loren! That is exactly why I've been looking for a dress like that! It's been in my head to have a dress like that!"

Sofia thinks. "Sit, now. *Prego!* Sofia is me! I am Sofia."

NeeNee sits, says, softly, "Sofia."

In the pan, the fish begins to hum "The Humming Chorus" as composed by Sofia's namesake Puccini, from *Madama Butterfly*.

———

I'm exhausted from my weight-loss ploys of either buying things one size smaller than I need so I can wear it once I lose some weight, or buying a size larger so I will look like I just lost some weight. Plus it's expensive. I'm tired of dressing strategically, dressing to hide my physical flaws, dressing to accentuate my positives, which in my case are my boobs and hips, and dressing to disguise my negatives, which are all the things that hold my boobs and hips together. Especially my belly.

My innocent Buddha belly.

Our sacred belly is what gives birth to the universe.

If not for her there would be no us. Every single one of us on this planet came from her, and yet we are told and sold and brainwashed into believing we must hide her, disguise her, suck it in. *Tone it up, muffin top.*

She is us and we are her.

A muffin is a food. Not a body part. When you go to the doctor with a pain in your stomach, she does not say: *Let me palpate your muffin. You have an ulcer in your muffin.* You do not get diagnosed with a muffin ache.

O, Buddha belly.

Also, upper arms. A lethal weakness. Every costume I've worn over the last ten years I've been adamant that there must be sleeves. I paid almost fifty dollars (plus tax) for a thing called a Sleevey Wonder that you wear underneath sleeveless dresses (but over your hidden push-up bra) so that the sleeveless dresses have sleeves.

Maybe we should all look like the Venus de Milo. You know. No arms at all.

Orange is the new black. Kale is the new spinach. Upper arms are the new vagina. Just another body part to keep hidden.

Dudes on noisy motorcycles truck along with their giant beer bellies out in front of them, and not one of them ever tries to balance out their silhouette by wearing a peplum. They don't consider wearing a deep V-neck to draw the eye upwards.

We give up. We hide. We dress to perpetuate our horrible, worthless state of wretched being that comes from a stupid pair of pants that feels too tight. This is why we see people in the grocery store wearing their pyjamas. The zombie apocalypse has arrived and they are wearing their flannels. Wandering aimlessly.

Once upon a time if you saw someone wandering around looking dishevelled in their pyjamas you assumed they had Alzheimer's disease and you called the police or the ambulance.

Why get out of bed at all? Let's just strap the mattress on, tie the pillow onto the back of our head.

The grocery store is traumatic at the best of times. *What if I see someone I know? What if I see them and they pretend not to see me? What if they see me and I pretend not to see them? What if I can't think of anything to say? What if I do and it's stupid? What if someone sees me hiding beneath the cabbages?*

I'm speaking telepathically. Hear me.

Everything is the new something. Sixty is the new fifty. Fifty is the new forty. Forty is the new thirty. By the time I hit seventy it will be the new seventeen and I'll be back in high school and going through the nightmare of adolescence and acne and emotional turmoil and bullying, which I barely survived (and would not have if not for Pittman), so why in God's name would I want to go back and relive that all over again?

Old is the new young. That's why there's Botox. Botulism for your face. It's a poison and they stick it into your face with little needles so it paralyzes you and you can't move a muscle. They can do this thing now where they suck all the fat out of your backside with a big needle and inject it into your lips. I might end up with cellulite on my face, but at least no one will have to bend over to kiss my arse.

Aging is the single greatest gift we are given at the moment we are born. And then we fight it all the way.

The only reason I do yoga is because I imagine myself walking down the street and people stopping to stare and say: *She does yoga.* I hate yoga. I hate everyone in my yoga class. I hate my yoga teacher. I hate the people who know how to do it all. I hate the people who flop around and accidentally touch me. I want to murder everyone. And while I'm nimbly stabbing everyone, I want to look like someone who does yoga.

Yoga teaches you to have a mantra for your life. A meditation. It can be: *I Am*. Or: *I am here, now*. It's your own personal mission statement. I haven't found mine yet.

When you are doing yoga people tell you, "Keep your monkey mind in your head." Or something like that. It means don't let your mind wander. But that's not easy when your head is floating around outside of your body with your mind in it. My monkey mind is only happy when it is outside my body. My monkey mind is having a way better time than me. It is out there, swinging on the chandelier, racing up and down the walls, singing and wearing red lipstick and not shaving its legs.

The final pose of every yoga class is called *Savasana*. Corpse Pose. Which means: yoga kills me.

Mythical myths

IN VENICE I HEAR about a mythical female gondolier. A rumour that one has been seen. She is mysterious, alluring, and slightly dangerous. She glides up in the mists, takes her passengers, accepts no money, and then glides away again.

For centuries, gondolier licences have been passed from father to son only. Gondoliers have rigorous training and are considered elites of the workforce of Venice. Real Venetians never ride in gondolas.

Venice is a saga. A century's worth of description isn't enough, as history has proven.

No matter how often one may land there, trample all over it, buy it, eat it, ooh and aah over it, no one has ever really truly been to Venice.

Oh, La Serenissima. Oh, La Dominante.

There are aspects of Venice unknown even to itself.

So ancient as to be completely forgotten by itself.

Such as the place where we stayed.

We step off the *vaporetto* at our chosen district of San Marco.

We scramble though a labyrinth of canals, bridges, and narrow alleys for two hours, trying to decipher the directions offered on the website for our accommodations. Nothing makes sense. These directions turn out to be a fiction written for revenge and amusement by a resentful porter.

Our Residenza Ca' San Marco isn't what we envisioned.

We push a battered intercom button, and after a pause an irritated voice says, "Wait there!" After a few minutes the resentful porter arrives and leads us through the maze to what seems to be a very lovely hotel. There, we're admonished by the concierge and told that this very lovely hotel isn't for us. No free breakfast for us. We are led through a thunderstorm to a dark weeping door and admitted into Hades.

In that moment, a great life lesson is learned.

Our room is so tiny that best-friend-in-all-the-world and I have to take turns changing our minds.

We find comfort in knowing that at least we are miserable in Venice, which is an excellent place in which to be miserable.

We wander into a little dress shop and are immediately tailed by two security guards and two beautiful, pouty salespeople who eye us up and down as we finger silky dresses with sweaty fingers and wonder aloud why there are no price tags in sight. The dresses don't look like anything to crow about, but they're so valuable they're chained to the floor, as if they were dangerous creatures. *Fuck you, dress*, I whisper to one. *I don't need you.*

As we leave, they slam the door behind us and lock it.

The gondoliers drift by, oblivious to all.

Lost in Venice

A FEMALE CODFISH CAN lay millions of eggs and not even once worry about whether or not her breasts have deflated or if her frown lines give her a bitchy resting face.

A female codfish can have millions of babies and then go study brocade fabric making in Sicily, and no one says she's an old maid, spinster codfish. No one says she's a bad mother.

This is why the cod is so amiable about being eaten.

—

The two women have eaten their fill of the singing fish, the last echoes of the song lingering in the air along with the delicious aromas.

The sound of the water coming in under the door of Sofia's World-Famous Trattoria has the hypnotic quality of a magical fountain. Sofia has shut the door, thinking it would deter the flow. It has not.

The *acqua pazza* is not the only dish. It is the starter. It rests on its laurels. All the delicious layers recline in erotic disarray: the olives, the citrus. The food is the dance and the prelude to the dance.

There is a bowl of pasta that Sofia has made with her own two hands, with the flour and the eggs and the olive oil and the secret hint of garlic. She made that pasta so tenderly. It rustles softly, with fresh clams and whatever else she threw in that pot.

"Fresh, fresh, fresh!" Sofia sings.

The basket that is, itself, bread, has been chewed around the edges in decorative patterns. Everyone in the neighbourhood envies the idea of a basket made of bread, but no one steals the idea because they know Sofia will kill them if they do.

"Eat more! You so lucky I do not murder you with a glance." Sofia grabs a broom and begins to sweep the water out the door.

She says, "Is inexplicable. You waltz in, la la la, coming in and interrupting my prayer. Now I say, 'Lift your feet, you don't want to get wet.'" She taps NeeNee on the legs with the broom. "Can you believe the nerve of how that Restaurant of No Food is built? A menu? I don't get it. Are they all a baby? Because a menu, it is for babies. Only babies want to know what is the food, what is the wine, which wine, pair that wine. I tell the people what I have for them. I do not have the *menu de touriste*. I tell them if that's what they are looking for, then they can go outside and lick the green scum off the side of the canal, because I would not sully my reputation with that *menu de touriste*."

NeeNee says, "They probably *would* lick the green scum off the side of the canal if you told them."

The water is not deterred by being swept out the door. It comes back in, rising a little higher in defiance. Sofia gives up. She pulls a priceless (stolen) embroidered stool close, it being the only other thing in the place to sit on. The wine pours itself. Sofia says, "This is Sofia's World-Famous Trattoria. It mean: you eat what I tell you, and that is the *acqua pazza* with the cod. This *acqua pazza* is so good, it make you want to dance. You must dance! Dance for the *acqua pazza*."

Off come the black tights and the nun shoes. She jumps up and splashes around in the water, pulling NeeNee to her feet. They dance in the rising water, which sloshes well over their ankles. It's cold, the water, but the trattoria is warm and cozy.

NeeNee says, "I remember when my mother said to me, 'You know, you could be pretty if you try.'"

Sofia says, "You can never wait to be seen by someone else. That is stupido."

NeeNee says, "May I ask you something? How do you know that the last time you ever make love is going to be the last time?"

—

NeeNee looks for her purse, which she finds floating under the table, sodden. She pulls out a small photograph with a name embossed on the back. Sofia slowly pulls the veil from off her face, throwing it back so that she looks like a bride dressed in black. She examines the photograph, that of a pious-looking sculpture, an incandescent woman with a transparent veil. She reads the name of the sculptor on the back of the photo, which slowly dissolves in her fingers from the damp.

"You look for Giovanni Strazza? You look for a sculptor, some dead sculptor? Pah! This is Italia. When we walk on the street we crunch the bones of a million dead sculptors. We drink some wine now. I don't do the tiny talk. The small chatter. Be quiet and eat. I tear this up for you."

Sofia tears the photograph into tiny pieces.

And thus it was that a veiled virgin held a photo of another veiled virgin and neither one of them knew.

In the embers

MY MOTHER IS IN tears. My mother is in mourning. Her worst fears were nothing before this. My mother says her blood pressure can't take it. She is grieving my death.

Hers is a double-double cup of grief. Though dead, I have the audacity to be up and about, instead of lying down, behaving as a good dead person should.

Come out, come out, wherever you are!

When I was alive, I was dead.

Now dead to my mother, I live.

—

I was besotted with Pittman. She was besotted with *The Veiled Virgin*. We went to see her as often as we could: morning, noon, and night. It was nothing for us to ring the doorbell of Presentation Convent at midnight.

Sister. Sister. We want to see The Virgin.
You were just here this morning.
Yeah, but we need to see her again.
Ye are nothing but the pure torments.

To their credit, the nuns escorted us in each time like we were going to an audience with the pope. Each time like the first time. On one of our late-night visits we encountered two younger nuns walking down a corridor supporting a third aged nun between them. They all wore elaborate habits, dark black, wimples with white crowns, the luxurious weight of expensive fabric swishing as they walked. The older nun was weeping. "I'm so afraid of the dark," she said. "So terribly afraid." The other two were gently shushing her. It seemed as if they were walking a toddler. I remember it well.

⸺

Come out. Come out. Wherever you are. Wherever you may be.

It is a precarious business, this being human. Dying attracts so much judgment. I am dead. I walk as the dead walk. I talk as the dead talk. Others are dead like me.

My mother says that people don't want to be forced to look at us. She says that no one wants to look at that. At us. At me. She says I am killing her.

Already dead, my remains rot and peel away. I am flayed and flayed again as in ancient times when my sort were witches. Bitches. I am bare to the bone, Bird, no flesh remains, but there are many places within where there is space and peace, where worlds are born, die, are born again.

They fear me. I fear myself. Selves.

—

The room is draped in burgundy velvet. She sits quietly in one corner, beneath a glass dome. She is exquisite, pristine, of white Carrara marble with a sparkling sheen. The veil is sculpted in such a way that it appears transparent, eternally protecting her visage, her modestly downcast eyes.

She waits.

We stare in silence until we can see her breath whispering through the veil. She's not a demure, floating-around Virgin with her heart hanging outside of her body. She's a mysterious, beautiful Virgin who looks as if she would like to tell you the antidote for life.

After our time with *The Veiled Virgin*, we'd careen through Bannerman Park, sometimes with a stolen bottle of Baby Duck, picking cigarette butts off the ground, pretending we didn't speak English, pretending we were Italian exchange students. When The Leaning Tower of Pizza opened up downtown, we were convinced it was a sign that we were meant to go to Italy to find the twin, The Other.

Pittman loved the nuns. She indulged her fixation on Mother Teresa and made endless plans to go to Calcutta to join up and be a holy acolyte who tended to lepers. I knew she would. She promised to wait until after we went to Italy, because neither one of us was sure if Mother Teresa approved of worldwide gallivanting. She asked me many times to go with her to India, to just take off, jump down the rabbit hole.

I was a scared cat.

—

I dream of Italy. It will never be for the likes of me. I dive inside all the pasta and all the wine in my mind. The headlines will scream: *Italy runs out of pasta and wine.*

I will eat Italy. I will drink Rome.

I will cast a spell so that Pope Francis falls in love

with me. He will say: *Oh, Bird. I want to marry you.* And I will say: *Oh, Frankie. I want you to marry me, too. I want you to marry me to my beautiful self.*

An Italian waitress, who burns in the same way as me, might say my name.

I was mine before we met. I was mine before either of us was born. I was mine from the beginning of time and will be until the end.

I am mine.

I am hers without knowing her yet.

We are soul monsters together, devouring, encompassing, enveloping, waiting for my self to arrive.

I live here. In the embers.

Dresses don't give a fuck

NOW IS THE TIME for everyone to come out.

Come into the light. Not into the hateful glare of the overhead fluorescents in the department store dressing rooms. Come into the light of *It's my body and I'll eat pie if I want to*. No more dressing strategically, dressing for success, dressing for one's age.

After a lot of meditation on that long, rainy, lonely night on my yoga mat, I decided my body shape is the *Fuck You* body shape.

I'm starting my own diet franchise. It's called "Eat Something." Here's how it works: People pay me money. I put all the money in my bank account. And then people call me and say, "Oh my God, I hate my body but I'm so hungry, what do I do, what do I do, what do I do?"

And I will say, "Eat something. Eat some pudding."

People will call me and say, "Oh my God, I need a snack, but like a healthy snack, what can I snack on?"

And I will say, "Eat a carrot dipped in pudding. Eat chocolate pudding, rice pudding, pease pudding, steak pudding, moose sausage pudding."

People will call me and say, "Oh my God, I ate so much, I'm full, I can't eat another bite."

And I will say, "Aha!"

—

We women are all gay. Because we dress to please other women.

Some garments are labelled one size fits all. This means that the same garment will fit someone who is a size zero. And someone who is not.

It is roughly the size of a small sock.

—

The next morning, having missed my opening, missed my friends, missed out on so much, I went through my closet.

I donated all the things I didn't wear and all the things I had to accept that I was never going to wear again. My Girl Guide uniform. I wept when I gave away the size five wraparound dress I had not fit into for twenty years.

But it did not weep for me. Because dresses have no feelings and do not give a fuck what size they are. Devil does not even care!

I got drunk and threw out the scales.

And now I only wear my best stuff. Wear all your best stuff all the time. People save their best stuff for special occasions. This is arse foremost. "I can't wear it all the time, I'll wear it out." Well, yes. Wear it out into the world, and every day will be a little bit more special. This goes for jewellery, hats, scarves, and underwear. I do not want to adhere to the "less is more" policy. Does Mother Nature tell the rose bush to grow but one flower?

Less is not more. More is more.

What if we all decided to rebel against the global industry that makes billions of dollars every single day, maybe even every single minute, maybe even every single second, by convincing women that there is always something about them, about us, that must change?

They're finally taking the taxes off the feminine protection products. We should all get a lifetime rebate on that. All that money for a box of pads with no prize in the bottom of the box. You can stand stupefied before the dazzling array you see laid out before you in a store: slim, extra-slim, regular, super, deodorant, non-deodorant, with applicator, without applicator, plastic applicator, cardboard applicator, panty liners, oval, thong, long, thin, maxi, maxi with wings. Do we wear it or fly it home?

The world wants women to be small. And protected.

If we rebelled, there'd be a shortage of bread. We'd all be fat and happy. Why is bread the enemy? If music be the food of life, a loaf of bread, a jug of wine, and thou, thine own self. Thou cannot live on bread alone; give us this day our daily bread; poetry is what we do to break bread with the dead; the sky is the daily bread of the eye; the musical group Bread.

Bread is the most sensual of foods. It's sexy. It's yeasty, warm, and soft. It swells up and rises. You put butter on it and lick it off. Then you lick your fingers. If you plant your bread crumbs you can grow loaf after loaf of homemade bread on your windowsill.

There's no such thing as gluten-free music, or poetry, or theatre, or books (although e-readers might be gluten-free books and should probably be banned).

—

I'm giving up pretending not to be depressed. I'm unpretending about my depression, because it's fucking depressing.

I like the thought of being in the grocery store and someone says, "Hi, how are you, fine I hope?" and then I say, "No, crap, shit, fuck."

The first psychiatrist I saw was a big round guy. He sat in a chair. He said: *Kneel down on the floor and pretend to be a cow.*

I did it. I was too young at the time to know exactly why it was wrong, the creepy, kinky, fetishist pervert. I did know it wasn't right. Little did I know I was on the road to cow greatness on the stage. Little did he know that I'd persevere.

Inside that cow costume with the udder hanging out, I had tears in my eyes. I wanted to howl. I wanted to cry, have a nervous breakdown, and then have a breakthrough, but all I could do was say: *Moo. Whither thou goest?*

I'm done being a too-good nudnick.

Whither thou goest? I ask myself.

La Dolce Vita

THE SWEETEST DAY IN Venice begins when we take the *vaporetto* to the Ponte dell'Accademia. By now we are *buongiorno*-ing and *grazie*-ing like pros. I'm working my way up to a *Prego!*, but it's best to move cautiously with these things. We sit in the early morning drinking exquisite coffee in exquisite sunshine served to us by an exquisitely rude woman. We sit next to professorial types who chain-smoke, exhale their smoke at us, and have espresso flowing through their veins.

Native Italians are easily discerned from the madding crowd. Most Italians wear black and are extremely beautiful, even and especially the older ones. They're the only species on this planet able to cultivate an expression that says, *Come hither you know you want me but if you do I will snarl and smack you one so shut up*. They stride around with lit cigarettes drooping from fingers and lips, even if they don't happen to smoke. They're incredibly stylish in the way that a panther is stylish just before it eats you.

This makes them irresistible. Panthers and Italians. Same thing.

Having escaped from our Hovel Hades in San Marco, we discover that the area surrounding the Ponte dell'Accademia is our style of Venice. One can easily imagine Ezra Pound sitting in a café working on *The Pisan Cantos*. One can easily imagine knowing what *The Pisan Cantos* are. In the academic district, my IQ immediately zooms upward. Artists, musicians, and random elegant people swan around creating, singing, dancing, or just simply being the epitome of sexy.

My conversation with best-friend-in-all-the-world, overheard by innocent Italians who pretend not to understand English:

> *So, is this where that famous artist is from?*
> *Which famous artist?*
> *Pistachio.*
> *His name isn't Pistachio.*
> *I know.*

On this day we visit the Peggy Guggenheim exhibit, which is in Peggy Guggenheim's palazzo, next to Peggy Guggenheim's grave, which is right beside the graves of all her little Guggenheim dogs.

Best-friend-in-all-the-world finally got to meet her Pistachio. He didn't disappoint.

The Guggenheim experience is best described as *Alice in Wonderland* for everyone. The art is extravagant. We try to move in, but our idea to pose as living art doesn't go over too well.

By chance, we discover a rare store that still makes lace, owned by Silvano Lasala. His son, Alberto, is there on the day we wander in. He tells us that this art form is dying out in Italy and that the store will likely die with his father. Best-friend-in-all-the-world is enamoured with a blue tablecloth that we are informed sells for over two thousand Canadian dollars. At that moment even she is speechless. There are rolls and rolls of priceless lace scattered over ancient tables. Alberto is also a renowned artist. This being Venice, we could never find our way back to the store again. That was good with me because I would hate to have to explain how some of that priceless lace fell into my pocket. In any case, the best way to find things in Venice is not to look for anything. It will find you, if it wants to.

Which is how something quite unexpected happens to me when best-friend-in-all-the-world decides she wants to spend the evening gambling at the elegant casino. It's a very beautiful place but very boring if one isn't into blackjack or roulette. I leave to wander the streets of Venice, then my friend the thunderstorm rolls in from Lucca.

I get lost, of course, the water teeming like a waterfall. I can't find our hovel. I stumble along, sopping, in tears of frustration.

I see her before she sees me. She is lounging in the doorway of the tiniest restaurant I have ever seen in my life, looking for all the world like Sophia Loren.

I ask her where she got her dress.

Gondoliers in love

THE THUNDERSTORM THROWS FORTH a fresh torrent of hailstones. Venezia has never seen the like of a storm like this. In the Piazza San Marco, the sculpted saints daintily lift their robes and climb to the top of the basilica. At The Restaurant of No Food, the tables and chairs are beginning to float away with angry patrons clinging to them.

There is a reason why nothing in Venezia goes in a straight line. The canals take this opportunity to rearrange themselves on a whim known only to goddesses. There is no use persisting in seeking logic.

Sofia, who normally tells her patrons to stay home and read a book, to go and get needles and stick them in her thumbs because that is how much fun she is having, smiles. The earth shifts slightly. Tremors are felt in remote places. Brimstone Head, an island off an island in the middle of the Atlantic, erupts with a geyser of lava. NeeNee's Google Map quivers and deletes itself from her phone. Venezia does not believe in Google Maps.

Sofia takes the measure of the rising water. The torrent of tides does not erase the torrent of fresh chatter that only she can hear emanating from the ceiling. She again begins to pray.

"I pray to Santa Sophia Loren. Are there flowers? No. Is the priest contracted for the service? No. Are there mourning clothes for the wake? No. And all that gondolier can do is look at me and weep and bite his nails."

She gestures to the ceiling, pointing to where NeeNee can see nothing.

NeeNee picks up the basket made of bread and eats more. The bread is so sexy, so yeasty, so soft. She cocks her head in the manner of a dog, earnestly trying to divine what Sofia wants her to see.

Sofia grabs a hunk of bread for herself.

"If the tourista come into my trattoria and say the words gluten-free? I ask them, 'What is gluten-free?' Ha ha. I take that bread on them, and I throw it away. Out the door with it. Out I throw it, like that. Out into the canal. Then I tell them: 'Now you are for sure gluten-free.'"

Sofia and NeeNee are still now, the water licking at their legs. Sofia brushes a strand of silvery lavender hair from NeeNee's face and whispers, "Oh, dear Santa Sophia Loren. Why the gondolier licence got to go to the next boy? It don't matter that I am the oldest. It go to the next boy. That's the way the stupido law is. But I want it. Si, I am 'a gay.' But I want to be the first 'a gay' girl gondolier. I do not tell just anyone I am the only 'a gay' in all of Italia. In Italia when you say you are 'a gay,' it is the same as if you say: 'Oh look, here come the Four Horsemen of the Apocalypse swooping down for the Rapture. So long, it was nice almost knowing you.'"

Sofia gazes into the eyes of the only other "a gay" she has ever known in her entire life.

"That stupido gondolier, he say to me: Why you have to be 'a gay'? Why you can't just be depressive like the rest of us? What for you want that gondola licence for?"

A surge of current rattles the table. The silver cutlery and embossed dishes slide into the water. NeeNee gestures as if to retrieve them, but Sofia gives a sensual shrug.

"Cutlery? Pah. We can live without that. That is what the bread is for. Only the tourista eat the pasta with the spoon. That is amateur. I do not slave over that pasta so people can eat it with a spoon. They use a spoon, I murder them in their sleep."

Each one of them notices that they are now holding hands without recollecting exactly when or how.

"Pah! That gondolier say if I am 'a gay' then I am dead to him, and then I say he is dead to me, haha, and now he is gone and I am vowed not to plan no funeral until I get that licence, and I am not getting the licence, so there can never be no funeral. What do I have left now? I got a sinking building and a pair of rubber boots."

Sofia guides NeeNee to stand on the chair. She herself stands on her stool.

The noise from The Restaurant of No Food is still audible beneath the teeming rain. Some of the patrons are screaming, others are drunk and oblivious, unwilling to give up a seat coveted for so long it is worth drowning for. One of the drowning patrons, it turns out, is the wealthy mogul who was supposed to be Sofia's one guest. He allowed himself to be diverted by the pulsing disco and macho waiters. He now regrets it very much. Happily for Sofia, he had prepaid his six-figure deposit.

Sofia says, "For so long, this ghost, he tortures me."

To both their surprise it is NeeNee who kisses Sofia and not the other way around. The disembodied voice from above is outraged and yells, but Sofia, for the first blissful time in a long time, does not hear it.

Marvel now

A FUNNY THING HAPPENED while I lay on my yoga mat waiting to die.

I didn't die. I dozed off and I woke up to Pittman saying my name.

I decided to not go gently into that good night. I don't believe in death. I'm not going. They can tell me to let go all they want, that stuff about it's okay to move on and you're better off out of it, but they can blow me. I'll be telling them to step away from the ventilator. Don't you touch that plug! Put that plug back in the wall! I'm not going to wake up dead one day to find someone who doesn't know me doing the eulogy and someone who didn't like me weeping over my coffin. I can't go. I'm not going. I have to be waked for one day each in every dress in my closet. That's at least two hundred days of being waked. It's in my will.

I have my own defibrillator.

The things people say about you when you're dead. Like: *She's dead*. As if dead people have no feelings.

There's too much time set aside for being dead and not enough time for living. I'm going on strike against death until this inequity is reversed. I spent all day searching for yesterday, the drops of my past, wanting to rearrange the view. I do it every day. I do it every night, trying to see the future retroactively. But with no action.

Delayed reactions. Can't get no satisfactioning. Buried in clothes I will never wear.

—

I got up and rummaged around until I found the elephant hair bracelet she had given me forty years earlier.

I went to the hospital, to emergency, and I had to wait for at least six hours, or it could have been sixty years. Finally, one of the nurses spoke to me and said, "What seems to be the problem?"

I said, "My heart. I think it's broken."

Suddenly I was surrounded by nurses and they started shouting out, "Stat! Stat! Lady here with a broken heart! Stat!" And they called out, "Quick! Get the cart! Get the cart!"

And they put me on a gurney and wheeled me so fast through all the corridors, and the nurses all surrounded me like white clouds speaking in crisp tones of comfort.

"Oh, honey. You hang in there. We are not going to lose you. We are not!"

"Quick, get the cart!"

They brought the cart of wine and cheese. Then they took an X-ray of my heart. Here it is. You can clearly see the fractures. And this is the cast, which they put on my heart.

And I walk around like this now: *Oh! Be careful! My heart!*

Oh, yeah, gee, I didn't see your cast. Sorry.

That's okay.

If you get a broken heart, go to the hospital and demand they put you on the heart attack ward. And if it's really bad, they can put you on life support for a while, just for a little while. And take painkillers, too. In ten years' time you'll look at photos of yourself and marvel at how young and lovely you were.

Why wait the ten years? Marvel now.

Puccini sings

IN LUCCA, I LEARN the art of seduction.

I perfect my stalking of Oliver. Oliver of the dark eyes and mournful gaze. Oliver of the soulful looks and come hither sighs.

Oliver is an Italian beagle doggy with floppy ears and a husky bark. He's an Italian beagle because he's a beagle who's from Italy. He was born and raised in Italy. This makes him an Italian beagle.

He runs the villa at Il Borghino. Each day I watch him as he embarks on his solitary and dogged (no pun intended) rounds of the grounds and surrounding hills and valleys. I approach him with overeager pleas: *Come here, Oliver! Good boy, Oliver! Come on over here, Ollie!*

He sometimes stops and stares for a moment, regarding me with his clever, soulful eyes. They say:

I am an Italian doggy. Why are you speaking to me in English when I am an Italian doggy?

He barks and runs away. But not too far away. He runs a little bit then stops to peer coyly over one furry shoulder before barking and running off a little farther.

He says: *Alas. If only you were the one I have been dreaming of for all of my doggy years. The one who would complete me. The one who would truly understand me. I am an Italian doggy trapped in a vegetarian yoga retreat. Do you perhaps have any bacon in your pocket?*

At breakfast sometimes I see him peering furtively through the glass doors of our little breakfast room, his eyes big and pleading.

At evening meditation, while I'm supposed to be at one with myself, my monkey mind is outside running in slow motion through fields of lemons with Oliver by my side, his floppy ears floating behind him in the breeze. My imaginary dog named Devil runs with us. We run and run and then picnic beneath the lemon tree on bacon bits and wine.

I tell Oliver that I spend hours wandering the narrow cobblestone streets of Lucca, trying to find the Piazza Bernardini. Every time I arrive at exactly where it's supposed to be, it's exactly not there.

Oliver stares. Devil sighs.

A direct approach is too straightforward. I'll have to invent another way to find the piazza, to catch it off guard.

—

There's a cuckoo in Lucca whose sole pleasure is to unleash a wondrous and melodic refrain upon the innocent yogis of Il Borghino. This tiny creature flies many miles to arrive outside our villa each day just before dawn. It chimes, exactly like a Swiss cuckoo clock. Except, unlike a Swiss cuckoo clock, which will only ever chime up to twelve times and then stop, the industrious Italian cuckoo will chime enchantingly on and on and on until I open my window and throw a lemon at it.

Not to hit it, of course. Not on purpose.

This to him is as bouquets thrown to the stage. He flies away to his next gig. But he will return on the morrow.

I go outside and retrieve my lemon.

Lemons in Italia are robust and glow with a shade of yellow so intense that to gaze upon them with the naked eye is to risk going blind. Similarly, the oranges here are evocative of the lengthy burning sunsets of Mars.

I've become a lemon and orange thief, a lemon and orange hoarder. I creep along the neighbouring villas in the morning mists.

I never knew before that the orchards and groves here are protected by electric fences.

—

It's possible there's a more enchanting place balanced somewhere between this world and the next.

It's possible there's a more captivating Italian-beagle-doggy-who-longs-for-bacon. A place where a little dog and a little Downward-Facing Dog can lift your heart.

A certain Italian-beagle-doggy-who-longs-for-bacon finally succumbed to my offers of ear scratching and lounged beside me for minutes at a time beside the pool.

It's possible there's another place on earth where the trees are so kind as to deposit your morning orange directly upon your doorstep.

—

Once Mrs. 'Arris has her couture gown, it turns out not to be as wonderful as she had thought. Like Mrs. 'Arris, I'm discovering the search for my dream

Sophia Loren dress is sweeter than actually finding the dress itself. There are many wonderful things about Italy that can only be found when lost, with the map turned upside down, and the even sweeter realization that although I'll never pass this way again, I'll wear these experiences upon my heart and face and hips. The most beautiful garment ever made. My body.

—

It's possible there's a doppelgänger for this country, one where the food is as delicious and flavourful, where a slice of tomato with a drizzle of oil and a sprinkle of fresh basil is so beautiful a person would starve rather than eat it.

But eat it you will, and you will weep while doing so. You will awaken to find a fresh orange dropped on your doorstep. Then a tree will fling another one at you and you'll weep again because, dear God, so much wonderful food.

I concede all of these possibilities.

I know in my heart that there'll never be another journey like this journey: intrepid, conquering, compassionate, triumphant, lively, alive.

Together my selves are greater than the sum of my parts.

Some of my parts are stronger than they were before.

There's an Irish folk song called "The Parting Glass."

> So here's a health to the company
> and one to my lass,
> Let's drink and be merry all out of one glass,
> Let's drink and be merry, all grief to refrain,
> For we may or might never
> All meet here again.

I won't say goodbye. I'll see you on the other side.

I made it up

I'VE GOT A PRICELESS collection of push-up bras. Never mind raising my breasts. You can raise the dead with these things.

They're made of wire, steel, bone, sutures, and Labradorite. This leads to false advertising when certain body parts appear to be slightly larger and perkier than they actually are. Metric tons of pressure fastened around your chest. Marvels of modern engineering. How they work is that every available ounce of fat is sucked off your body and shoved up under your chin. You can be guaranteed they were never tested out on animals. When I wear one, parts of me appear in a different time zone.

This one cost me fifty-six dollars plus tax at Victoria's Secret. Victoria's secret is that bras are a big rip-off for women. Fifty-six dollars for an item of clothing to be worn underneath other clothing. The most expensive bra I own cost me two hundred seventy-five dollars. Plus tax.

There's no equivalent piece of clothing for men. I can't explain the sensation of wearing the push-up bra to a man, unless that man wanted pay two hundred seventy-five dollars to have his dangly bits attached to a forklift. Plus tax.

There was a matching fifty-six dollar thong to go with the push-up bra. Which I bought. I put it on one night before I went to bed, and when I woke up in the morning, I couldn't find it anywhere. I may need surgery. The doctor will wonder: *What was she trying to do with the dental floss?*

We can buy bras now that come with dual air bags. They've got little plastic sacks in them, and they come with a little bicycle pump. You blow them up until you achieve the size you want. Which is never the size you are. I don't know what happens if you get a blowout.

Also, they come with gel stuffing. And padding. And cellphone chargers.

We don't have to be fierce, curvy, real. We don't have to be curvy or straight or gay. Or anything at all. I'm learning to use my words. Out loud. Telepathy works best with spoken words.

When I was onstage, dressed as the biblical cow, with the udder hanging out, looking at the audience looking at me made me want to cry. I wanted to have the breakdown. I was the original mad cow.

A voice inside still going: *Nyah, nyah, nyah, you can't do that, you're stupid and no one cares and you're incredibly ugly and delusional, ha ha ha, you have delusions of relevance.*

And another voice going: *You don't want to go to Italy at all, you just want to stay home and eat Cheezies and watch* Downton Abbey *and cry.*

So I took the first voice, and I took the second voice, and I put them in one of those fucking faux Tupperware containers.

They're in the freezer. If I ever again need anyone to heap abuse and loathing upon me, I know where they are.

—

I became telepathic when the aliens came to visit me (which is part of the story I can't tell you). It's a difficult gift. It's useless to be telepathic in a world where no one else is. That's how you end up alone, because you're sitting there communicating all the time. Telepathically. And others aren't.

Unless it's an Italian taxi driver. Or a trattoria-owning Italian lesbian in Venice.

When you love someone, you can't let them go. But if you do and they come back, they're yours; if they don't, they're not. You can't shut the door, move on, get closure as the world demands. My monkey mind won't do that. My monkey mind is running in slow motion through a field of daisies with Oliver the Italian beagle singing *I'd like to teach the world to sing in perfect harmony.*

I was thirteen years old, walking along a dark lane on a dark night, surrounded by trees. No sound, not a star in the sky, not a breeze or a bug on the fly. I glanced up to see a large glowing golden ball of light hovering just above me.

An intergalactic firefly.

It was looking at me. I looked at it. No words were spoken and no sounds were made. It imprinted upon me and I imprinted upon it.

At the centre of its light was an image.

It might have lasted a moment, or maybe it was an hour or a lifetime that I felt that wonderful essence of being a pure soul love authentic being. A true self. Selves.

But it faded too quickly.

The next thing you know someone will want to build a shrine and there'll be a holy spring and I'll have to join a convent and be a nun and the Virgin Mary Mother of God will get all the credit for my story and someone will have to die.

It was the first time I experienced not being believed. But not my last.

Not long after that, Pittman showed up. She believed me without batting an eye and loaned me her book about Atlantis by Taylor Caldwell.

Nothing, save death, will ever knock me from my life again.

> *From the torrent, or the fountain—*
> *From the red cliff of the mountain—*
> *From the sun that 'round me roll'd*
> *In its autumn tint of gold—*
> *From the lightning in the sky*
> *As it pass'd me flying by—*
> *From the thunder, and the storm—*
> *And the cloud that took the form*
> *(When the rest of Heaven was blue)*
> *Of a demon in my view—*

When someone asks me, *Does this make me look fat?*
I say, *I love you.*

Love out of time

THE WONDERFUL THING ABOUT inhabiting a woman-loving female body is that it knows what it wants. It knows what it needs. Give it its own way. It knows how to give and receive. In rising heat, the thought of the caress is as intoxicating as the actual touch. Women know how to circle, graze, and tease. The hint is more delicious than the full story. The erotic ache can ripple into forever. The touch is so soft it feels like the dream of touch, a teardrop on an ocean surface, felt by the deep black below.

The seduction is shy but not tentative. It is as insistent and gentle as the ocean polishing sea glass from a jagged shard.

With eyes closed in the dark there is only sensation, lips grazing soft skin, softer flesh. All of it standing up, one upon a chair, the other upon a priceless embroidered stool. The water rises, it too longing to glide up those thighs.

Sofia's fingers trace Braille on NeeNee's skin. The embossed symbols appear and fade, appear and fade. They say, *We are a very sexy people. It is our curse. We are a people who find older women like you very sexy. We like our women mature, like you, like a ripe fruit, ready to burst. Your little Buddha belly, your everything.*

Time is in an eddy, chasing its tail. In the ocean the wild female cod swim deep, deeper, deepest, in a flamenco of mating. Flirtation is bypassed for blind sex. Female with female churn the deepest waters. The miraculous progeny of this orgasmic frenzy will grow to unheard-of sizes, develop with golden blue scales, and become the subject of folkloric tales and songs, as they will never be caught, and seen only rarely. They are born for one purpose only.

Sofia, whose greatest dream is to be the first and only female, "a gay" gondolier, is released from her bitterness. NeeNee, whose greatest affliction has been the unrelenting need to please others, pleases herself.

Across the canal, which is now no canal at all but a river of mischievous floods, the spotlight at The Restaurant of No Food falls. Fairy lights blow into the sky, where, still lit, they will come to rest on an abandoned pier, causing a yacht of American boaters to head directly for it and crash.

A thumping, grinding pelvic beat emanates from a pair of speakers even though they are completely submerged. The Bee Gees are singing a watery version of "Staying Alive," even though only one of them still is.

The standing-up lovemaking becomes slow, slower, slowest. Time stands outside of time, out of time. Anyone looking at them would think the two women were carved of stone, unmoving. Unless one stood and looked at them for a thousand years one dark and stormy night.

We drown for sure

"*SCOPARE.* IT ALL BECOMES so very fucked-ed up, so fast." This from NeeNee. She and Sofia have begun unconsciously mimicking each other in the manner of newly besotted lovers.

It floods and floods and floods. It seems to NeeNee and Sofia that maybe the world really is ending now, the Four Horsemen coming, the Apocalypse happening. Each one feels her heart bathed in sunlight, at direct odds with the weather.

Sofia says, "If we get washed out into the canal, we die for sure. No, we don't drown, it is not that deep. The vaporetto. The water bus, all the boats, they go too fast, no one stops for nothing, ever at all. Twenty-five people every day get run over in that canal."

NeeNee is happier than she's ever been in her entire life and only hopes that they can remain standing on this chair and this stool forever.

"That dead gondolier, my papa, won't let me have a minute of rest until I make it all better. He don't ever shut up, not even once."

Sofia gesticulates to the ceiling, pointing to where the ghost of her inconsiderate dead papa hovers. NeeNee looks and looks, at first seeing nothing, but then she begins to hear a faint buzzing underneath the watery turmoil, as if an angry wasp was trapped on the wrong side of a window.

"I see the dead, it run in our family," Sofia confides. "Yes, I see the dead people. See? See? And see? They are everywhere. I see you. You might be alive, but to me you don't look like you have been living too much."

NeeNee puts her arms protectively around Sofia, which causes the angry wasp to buzz louder.

The water, which has never risen this high ever before, rises higher still. Sofia realizes that although she's been praying and praying and praying to Santa Sophia Loren, Sophia Loren isn't answering back.

Sofia says, "The water come in. The water go out. It is worth nothing, I tell you. Working all of these years because that day led to this day when my papa is dead and will not rest or stop nagging me. In life he never spoke. In death, he don't shut up."

Venezia normally is the perfect place for a miserable person. It is built on pylons in a marsh and is slowly sinking, after all. This night, however, the canals are drunk with love. The basket made of bread goes floating merrily along and is eaten by a happy post-coital cod. In the distance they can see the silhouette of the Island of the Dead, a dark shadow on the horizon.

Sofia says, "In Venezia, we have no land, no earth, no soil, nowhere for to bury our dead. We have to take them to the Island of the Dead. Who will row the gondolier to the grave of the gondolier, I ask. Anyway, I don't know why he got to yell so much. He only has been dead ten years or so. Give or take."

The water goes rush, rush, rush. They get themselves up to balance on the table and watch as the chair and the priceless stool embark on their own adventures. The Restaurant of No Food is no longer there.

"I laugh, ha ha," Sofia laughs, "at that Restaurant of No Food. Look at how they are no longer there. The Village Peoples might be singing there, but it don't help. It serves them right with the just desserts. Always rubbing it in, it all over the place my nose."

Newfoundlandia and Venezia have fallen in love, more than a little. From the table, Sofia can reach a decanter of cognac on a shelf, and she pours them each a poem in a glass. She's been saving it for apocalyptic after-times such as this. A garden in a glass. In a pinch it can be used as a life-giving transfusion. People ask to be buried with it. Saint Peter can be bribed at the gate with it.

They toast each other. Sofia says, "I want to be buried on the Island of the Dead in Venice where everyone is above ground. And I want a glass of this and a little bell beside me. Just in case."

The angry wasp is buzzing most indecorously now. NeeNee can see what an effort it is for Sofia to block it out. NeeNee feels, at last, quite calm and in control. She knows very well how ghosts and angry voices can keep a human trapped in a maze of unhappy repetition and half-lived life. She also knows exactly what to do with the disembodied voices of the past. Therefore, she is not surprised to see a splendid gondola float directly up to the door of the trattoria and wait there.

They climb aboard.

Codfish in love

A FEMALE CODFISH CAN have millions and millions of those little cod babies, and nobody ever calls her a slut. She can swim away with another female codfish, and no one ever says anything about that. Because a fish is a fish is a fish.

NeeNee sits calmly in the gondola. Sofia sits beside her. At first they almost tip over. For all of her bravado and longing, Sofia has never poled a gondola before. But that doesn't matter. The current is guiding them toward their destination.

NeeNee is holding a small cake tin. It contains the nattering voice of the dead gondolier. NeeNee knew exactly how to lure that nasty voice into the can, having done something similar with her own nattering voices not that long before. Now that the dead gondolier is being rowed to the Island of the Dead, he feels somewhat more fondly disposed toward his "a gay" daughter.

Not too much, though.

NeeNee is realizing that Sofia reminds her of someone, a long ago and far away someone. Someone who was her best friend, and first crush, in another life.

The thunderstorm graciously stopped the moment they stepped aboard the gondola. In the manner of great storms, it moved on to create havoc in other places. It returned to Lucca from whence it came.

―

A ready-made picnic was waiting for them, conveniently untouched by the storm. Champagne with proper glasses. Foods for fingers and the licking of fingers and the stroking of lips. Sofia is feeding NeeNee anchovies.

The anchovies are soft with olive oil, and slippery.

"Life is like a anchovy."

"I always thought anchovy was a paste that came out of a tube."

"Tube?"

"Anchovy? Is it like a capelin?"

"I don't know from capelin. Anchovy do not come from out of a 'tube.' They come from out of the ocean.

They are not pleasant. You acquire the taste. No one tell you life is always going to taste good. You got to acquire that taste."

There is no speaking for a while as they eat, gluttonous, starving. Tomatoes dressed in the freshest oregano, mushrooms still speckled with dirt, bread melting under the weight of garlic and butter and cream.

"You blunder in like it is nothing at all. I think that Santa Sophia Loren finally send me a sign."

The first female "a gay" gondolier touches her own face with her greasy fingers, feeling her countenance to be soft, softer, softest.

"I tell you, this is something. You bring me the luck, with that smile."

The sky is brightening when they look up to see the Island of the Dead looming in front of them. They drink more champagne.

Santa Sophia Loren smiles down on the lovers as the gentle rocking of the gondola leads to another gentle rocking, the women curling into and over and under each other.

The tin can with the voice of the buzzing gondolier falls overboard, unnoticed, and sinks to the bottom of the ocean. It is immediately surrounded by the discontented bones of one Giovanni Strazza, and there they remain to this day, buzzing and nattering their displeasure into eternity.

—

NeeNee slips a tiny silver bracelet around the wrist of Sofia Giacomo Antonio Domenico Michele Secondo Maria.

"You will come back to me, my one true love, Newfoundlandia. I put a bandage on my heart until we see each other again. When you leave, I am still the only 'a gay' in all of Italia. But not so lonely now."

"You will come to Newfoundland as soon as possible, of course, my sweet Sofia. My house is not very big, but I've always felt it was too big for only me."

"You will run Sofia's World-Famous Trattoria and I will run the gondola. Together we make this beautiful life."

"You can give Italian lessons and I can write and maybe we can open an Airbnb or something."

Between kisses and exhalations as delicate as a butterfly's wings, each is certain that they have convinced the other of the way forward, and that it will only be a matter of time before they are reunited. Time, however, has other matters more pressing.

They are blissfully unaware, NeeNee now wearing Sofia's dress, the dress of her dreams, so she can carry the scent of her lover with her wherever she goes.

—

When it is time to leave, I realize it is very difficult to get out of Italy. In every way. Most especially so because as we lifted off, I realized I had left behind a little piece of my heart.

As we are corralled through the throngs at security at Gatwick, I feel melancholy. Italy is behind me now. Home lies ahead. In between is the expanse of air and ocean where for another little while I'll be weightless before touching down.

Firefly's last breath

IN MY PLAY *BRAZIL SQUARE*, the taxi driver, Mr. Butler, proposes on bended knee to Mrs. Kent. He has a tiny ring with a genuine diamond chip and two tickets to Italy. She turns him down, and in his despair he drives away and dies in a tragic accident. The boarding house industry becomes obsolete. Mrs. Kent loses her memories, then her mind. She goes off her head. She ends up in a care facility where she believes the other residents are her boarders who have come back at last. She practices her Italian phrases, but the closest she ever comes is eating SpaghettiOs from out of a can. She forgets that she turned down her true love, Mr. Butler, because her late husband wasn't dead. He was an American soldier who married her during the war and then abandoned her in the aftermath.

I never lied. I only ever said he was late. Very, very, very late.

She still has her brochures, so worn that the pages feel like cloth. Sometimes in her dreams she finds a sanctuary at the top of the hill in Lucca, the one in the painting she used to have.

The marvellous actor Petrina Bromley, who brought Mrs. Kent to light, is one of the original Broadway stars of the worldwide phenomenon *Come from Away*. At this writing she, like the rest of us, is patiently waiting to see what theatre will be in our brave new world.

———

I was in my early twenties, struggling as a single parent in Corner Brook, working the midnight shift as a DJ at a local radio station, when Pittman called to tell me about the cancer. We weren't in touch very often by then, but we enjoyed that wonderful rare connection where a word a year was worth a million a day. She told me she was in treatment. The chemotherapy was making her hideously sick, and for this reason she was convinced it was working.

I flew to St. John's to see her. No one could have been prepared to see that beautiful being so emaciated, the hair finally thinned, not by shears, but by the drugs. She was unable to sleep without pain medication, and because everyone imprinted on her, she was surrounded by loving caregivers who tended to her, came when called with hypodermics of sweet relief. She was in the same house, which by now did have hot water and electricity. I was completely useless. I didn't know what to say. I prattled on about Elisabeth Kübler-Ross and the five steps of death and dying.

The last time I saw Pittman, she was skeletal, ravaged by the disease that did not care that she was too young. She gripped me by the wrist. She would not let me go. She dragged me through the blackest night.

She would not let me go.

Then we came over the rise of a very tall hill, maybe the tallest hill in all the world. It was like walking into a painting. The darkness slowly changed to green and blue. We looked down upon a vista of valleys, vineyards, and orchards. I smelled lemons and honey. I saw below a picturesque village surrounded by ramparts and closer to us a cluster of elegant villas, a beagle rolling on the grass. I turned to her and saw that she was restored to her old self, her wonderful, old, orphanated self. Pittman with the hair like a birch broom in the fits.

She smiled and said: *This is what it's like to die.*
Then she let me go.

———

Later that morning the phone rang and someone told me what I already knew. She didn't live to see her twenty-seventh birthday. She died on the exact date her mother had died, not that many years before.

I stood on that hill once more, a small lifetime later, that tallest hill in Lucca and saw for real what she had shown me.

She had given me a delicate silver bracelet, which she told me encased a single elephant hair. Proof. The firefly and the elephant.

If I had my time back, I'd draw things on your back and never take the quarter and never give up too soon. I'd put myself in your line of vision when you were looking at boys. I would take you by the hand. We would go to Calcutta, and you would be an unchaste nun, hunting for The Other in your spare time, when not tending to lepers.

I carry you, I carry you, as someone better than me once wrote. I found others along the way, but you were my first love.

———

At my next play opening, I sashayed into the fancy gourmet dinner. Devil may care. Head up. Chest out. Naked as a Puccini-singing songbird. Jiggling. I waved. Some people waved back at me. My own body the perfect garment.

I picked up a drink and looked at everyone looking at me. I looked down at myself and said, *Wow. I look great in this.*

Then the police came.

A journey

SIGHTINGS OF THE SILVERY blue cod flotilla guiding the lone gondolier across the Atlantic are put down to too much drink, too much oceanic sunshine, and a pathetic need for attention. Like the Loch Ness monster, the spectacle is never seen when there are sensible people around with sensible equipment to record the image.

The journey will recreate that of *The Veiled Virgin*, the Giovanni Strazza sculpture that traversed the same route in 1856. The passenger will arrive in St. John's on the very same day as *The Virgin*, December 4.

Picture a stern-faced goddess driving a chariot and you can envision Sofia as she faces the harsh Atlantic winds. The silvery cod are massive, all female, and they sing as they glide along the surface of the harsh water. They are led by the light of a blue sky, driven by a thunderstorm that follows closely behind, on its way to a new performance in a new land

—

I chased after the bushy-haired girl with the John Lennon glasses and the buck teeth, impossibly impossible, along a river of evers. The weeping man with the white hair and the pocket watch kept watch. The Puccini mad hatters tittered and drank champagne. I was intent on her, my pits stained in the heat. I chased her down hooks and crooks of forks in roads and down paths the cows had long forgotten. She dashed around a corner and by the time I careened behind her, she'd gone. Vanished. I was alone and lost in Lucca. I sat down on a stone bench and cried. I glanced up to see a stern stone angel pointing her sword to a tiny brass plate on an ordinary wall.

Piazza Bernardini.

Here I am. Where I've been all along.

Epilogue

I thought I'd put Pittman to rest. She was in my memories but not in my dreams. I would run into one of her younger sisters every now and then and feel the old love come over me in waves.

As the years passed, I went months without thinking about her, then more than that.

For my sixtieth birthday I went on another yoga retreat. I went to Cuba and danced salsa with beautiful strangers while God's Thumbnail glowed in the inky Cuban sky.

I spent a day on a sandy beach gathering worn and precious sea glass, in greens, blues, ambers.

I came back to Canada, unrolled my yoga mat, and poured the sea glass on the mat in a pretty, sandy clump.

That night I fell asleep on my sofa and from out of nowhere she was in my dream.

She was holding my hand. We were wandering through a house full of family and friends. She told me again about the Sufi fable. I was wearing a dark purple, crushed velvet dress. Pittman had on a pair of faded Levi's and a fringed brown suede jacket.

I woke up to the sound of her saying my name. I found the sea glass on my yoga mat arranged into the shape of a firefly.

With a note:

Love,
Your life.

BERNARDINE ANN TERÁZ STAPLETON is an award-winning playwright, writer and performer of unique distinction. She has served as writer in residence at Memorial University, as playwright in residence with several national companies, and as artistic director of theatre festivals. Her plays are regularly produced nationally and internationally; her short fiction has appeared in *Riddle Fence* and the *Newfoundland Quarterly*. Previous books include *They Let Down Baskets* (co-author), *This Is the Cat*, and *Rants, Riffs and Roars*.